TALES OF THE RRIES

by Fred T. Morgan

ILLUSTRATED BY VIRGINIA INGRAM

To my three girls
Izzy, Rosie and "Trick"

Introduction

THE UWHARRIE MOUNTAINS of central North Carolina, remnants of the old Ocoees, are 500 million years old, ranking with the oldest mountains in the United States, possibly in North America. At one time they towered to 20,000 feet and rivaled the Swiss Alps in grandeur. Time has brought them to their knees, though they retain vestiges of conical summits, jut-jawed promontories, razorback and hogback ridges, and crusty, warty knobs which leapfrog and zigzag to the horizon.

Concentrated along both sides of the Yadkin River and its tributaries, the Uwharries are most prominent in Stanly, Montgomery, Davidson, and Randolph counties, though they spill over into adjacent counties, and their roots go even further.

Unending green forests cloak the Uwharries, taming the river gorges and smoothing the stark precipices and gashy ravines. Little brown roads and a few hard-surfaced ones snake through the region, along with streams, logging trails, and overgrown wagon roads. Big lakes spread out into the valleys and crevices of the hills. Unless you know just where to look, you are likely to miss most of the signs of early human occupancy and enterprise that give this land its heritage: dams, gristmills, fords, ferries, covered bridges, foot bridges, rock quarries, sawmills, and courthouse sites, as well as many, many old homeplaces, gold mines, and graveyards.

Indians lived in the Uwharries 10,000 years ago. These aborigines left rich records in the form of ceremonial centers (the Town Creek Indian Mound in Montgomery County has recently been restored), village and camp sites, fish traps, and artifacts galore. Even today, you can fill your pockets (baskets, too) with arrowheads, spear-points, pottery fragments, tools, and weapons left by the Indians in fields and along watercourses.

The Indians left reluctantly ahead of the white man's invasion, which began in earnest by the middle 1700's. Germans came from the northern colonies, while the Scotch-Irish, English, and French came down from Virginia and up the Cape Fear from the coast. It was during the first 150 years in which these pioneers were hewing a civilization in the wilderness that the stories in this volume were probably born.

Ghost stories permeate the Uwharries. They illumine the vast tapestry of Uwharrie folklore the way cloud castles dress up the sky. Catch a native oldster in the right mood, and he will talk with such color and fascination that you will wish you could stay for supper.

With the advantage of being a native, I have been able, through persistent prying, to pin a few ghostly hides to the wall. Yet, some of the exposed ghosts defy rationalization, identification, and classification, clinging to the aloofness and obstinacy that distinguish the true Uwharrie specimen. The ghosts with whom I have become acquainted still rankle me with their inexplicable quirks and eccentricities. Sometimes I get the feeling that I am the one under closest scrutiny.

The ghost stories in this volume are genuine, true in the sense that each comes directly from the folklore of the Uwharries, sifted through many generations of legends and oral tradition. I am deeply grateful to the many people throughout the Uwharries who were kind and patient enough to talk to me about their favorite ghosts.

Come with me now to meet and mingle with some of these colorful spiritworld characters who romp freely and uninhibitedly over this interesting land, and whose presence adds tone and zest to the gray-bearded Uwharries.

FRED T. MORGAN

Albemarle, N. C.
October 31, 1968

Contents

1	PEDDLER PAUL	3
2	PHANTOM FAMILY OF FIVE	9
3	THE HATCHET-SWINGING FIRE	15
4	THE FRIENDLY HANDS	22
5	HALF A PIECE OF GOLD	30
6	A BARGAIN WITH THE DEVIL	37
7	THE MIDNIGHT HUNTER	40
8	THE GHOST BY THE APPLE TREE	48
9	THE GHOST WHO PRACTICED DYING	54
10	THE GHOSTS OF THE KRON GOLD	61
11	PRIVATE CORRIHER'S GHOST	74
12	THE GHOSTS IN THE BURNING LOGS	79
13	MILLIE CROCKET	84
14	THE FIDDLER'S GHOST DANCERS	91
15	THE GHOSTS IN THE BIG BLACK CLOUD	97
16	THE GALLOPING GHOST	104
17	SAMBO'S WOODS	112
18	THE HEAVY HITCHHIKER	122
19	BLACK MATHIE	129
20	THE GHOST OF FOUNDERS' COLLEGE	140

Ghost Tales
of the
Uwharries

PEDDLER PAUL

TIME WAS WHEN itinerant peddlers circulated through the Uwharries, selling their trinkets, medical cures, and ofttimes their advice and services. For these vagabond salesmen, the rural people always had a cool drink of spring water and time for a few minutes' chat. Because they displayed an interesting assemblage of goods and brought fascinating stories and news of faraway places, they were, more often than not, welcome overnight guests in the country homes. Many of them, to reduce overhead and encumbrances, walked and lived off the land, carrying their merchandise in shoulder packs or hand satchels, and relying upon their wit and glibness to provide them with necessities.

Such a man was Irishman Peddler Paul.

He walked slowly now with his shoulders hunched slightly forward as if still straining against the burdensome shoulder pack, which had become so depleted that he carried it by his side as a hand satchel. A small, weak man in his forties, he knew well the rigors of the road, but he was quite unreconciled to the mysterious, wild Uwharrie country and its people. Underneath his air of bluster and salesmanship, he was a timid man, susceptible to impulsive action and instability in time of stress.

Sunset one late summer day caught him on a back road in the Uwharries with naught in sight but a run-down two-story house on the next hill. He stopped there and requested lodging for the night. The folks agreed to take him in.

It wasn't long before Peddler Paul realized that his choice of shelter had been an unfortunate one. There were no children in the home, and the elderly man and woman were a strange, silent pair with shifty eyes. Peddler Paul felt undertones of unpleasantness and mystery in the house. The whole atmosphere was one of hostility. His uneasiness was helped not at all by the abrupt entry of a third individual, a brawny, dim-witted giant, who took his seat at the supper table and proceeded to wolf down his food. The meal was eaten in silence.

No one asked the peddler for news of the road. Bedtime was suggested soon after supper. When Peddler Paul picked up his pack of merchandise, he thought he saw the grim-faced man and woman exchange glances. They escorted him up a narrow, twisting stairway to the second floor, the old woman carrying a kerosene lamp to light the way.

The old man pushed open a thick wooden door, shoved his blocky, brutal face close to Peddler Paul's, and growled, "In here."

Peddler Paul stepped into the dark room, and the heavy door creaked shut behind him. He heard a distinct metallic click as the door was bolted from the outside. Locked in! He became thoroughly alarmed now. What possible reason could they have for locking him inside except to do him bodily harm?

Striking a match, he found the stub of a candle on the old dresser and lit it. The feeble light showed him the sparse furnishings of the room. A rough bed, the covers mussed and smelly, stood against one wall.

He stood at the door and listened. He heard his hosts go back downstairs. There was a buzz of whispered voices. Then a door opened and slammed.

He went to the lone window and found it nailed securely shut. He looked out into the black night. The sight he saw made his heart skip a few beats and set his teeth to chattering.

Out there at the edge of the yard, framed in a circle of lantern light, was the dimwit he had seen at the supper table. The man swung a pick, digging a rectangular-shaped hole in the ground. A grave? It couldn't be anything else. And for whom? There wasn't much doubt about that either. Peddler Paul shuddered and trembled anew.

Back to the door he crept and listened carefully. The sound he heard put a chilly finger into his heart. Up the stairs came the unmistakable sound of a knife or an axe being sharpened against a grindstone.

Dizzy now with fright, he staggered to the bed and lay in shock on the foul covers. He had lain there for some time before he became aware of a new sound—this one close by.

A low moan or groan came from under the bed.

He jerked upright to listen. It came again, a forlorn and despairing groan. He was sure now. It came from under the bed.

He got up, lifted the candle from the dresser, threw back the low-hanging covers, and knelt beside the bed. The first thing he saw when he bent low and peered underneath was the glassy eyes and stark, cold face of a dead man.

Peddler Paul recoiled to the middle of the floor and sprawled there, stifling the scream of terror trying to burst from his mouth. He scrambled to his feet and cringed against the far wall. But even from there he could see the light of the fallen candle reflected in the glazed eyes of the dead man under the bed.

For moments he stood there, trembling against the wall, unable to wrest his gaze from the eerie glint of candlelight mirrored in the corpse's eyes. The thudding of the pick again registered faintly in his ears. He leaned over and peered out the window. The dimwit stood almost waist deep in the grave he was digging. The steady grating of the cutting tool being whetted against a rough stone continued to drift up the stairs.

As he started to approach the body again, a white vapor began to emerge from under the bed where the body lay. It swelled, waveringly, until it reached the dimensions of a man.

Peddler Paul clasped a hand over his open mouth to keep from screaming. He realized that this white wraith must be the ghost of the dead man under the bed.

The ghost stood between him and the bed.

"Don't be alarmed, friend," the ghost said. "I've come to help you. We've got to outwit this murderous old bastard and his hag wife. And we can do it if you'll put my poor, dead, mutilated body on that bed again."

When he could again command his faculties, Peddler Paul nodded

assent. The frost-colored apparition appeared friendly enough. He began to take heart.

Sickening as it was, Peddler Paul complied with the ghost's request. He pulled the stiff body out from under the bed, grasped it around the middle, and wrestled it up onto the bed. In doing so, he noted a gory stab wound in the chest and crusty dried blood all over the front of the white shirt. Every pocket of the corpse's expensive suit had been turned wrong side out.

The ghost looked on pathetically. "Sorry I can't help you, friend, but it would not do at all for me to help lug my own poor dead body around."

When the grisly task was accomplished, Peddler Paul, at the ghost's bidding, pulled the covers up under the chin of the corpse so that it resembled a man sleeping in bed.

Peddler Paul was still worried. "But they can tell it's you in the bed and not me," he said. "They'll notice the difference before I can get away."

"Leave that to me," the ghost said. "I've learned a trick or two in this ghosting business since my untimely initiation a few days ago. I'll handle that part of the deal."

They chatted for an interval, and from the friendly ghost Peddler Paul learned that the dead man had been a wealthy hardware merchant on his way through the Uwharries on horseback. He had been headed toward the western part of the state to establish a new store with the considerable sum of money he carried on his person. He had stopped here for lodging several nights ago, and the old couple had murdered and robbed him while he slept.

Stealthy footsteps ascended the stairway. The ghost motioned Peddler Paul to station himself behind the door, where he wouldn't be seen when it swung inward. He waited there, nerves taut as a banjo string. The ghost had vanished.

Muffled whispers came from outside the door. The bolt clicked back very softly, and the door swung in silently. Peddler Paul's heart thumped fast and heavy as he waited, hidden behind the open door, while the man and woman entered.

Satisfied that the man on the bed was fast asleep—as indeed he was—they crept closer.

"Hold the lamp up high, woman," the old man ordered in a calloused whisper, "so I can see how to git 'im with the first lick."

A long-bladed butcher knife, raised high in his hand, glinted wickedly in the lamplight.

Peddler Paul waited to see no more. Intent on their murderous business, the old couple failed to see him as, satchel in hand, he edged out the door behind them.

But as he moved out the door, he had one more shock. He glanced at the figure on the bed. It was not the face of the dead man that showed from under the covers. It was his own face! It was the face of Peddler Paul there in the bed. He was aghast. The ghost had kept his promise. But Peddler Paul wasted no time trying to figure out how.

He hurried down the stairs and across the room. Wildly encouraged by the success of the plan thus far, he jerked open the outside door. But there, facing him at the entrance, stood the dimwit, the giant of a man!

Peddler Paul almost collapsed. But freedom was so near that he choked back his fear and dashed madly by the hulking monster, who stood there slowly scratching his head in puzzlement.

Peddler Paul didn't stop running for miles. He was never seen in that area again.

But somewhere in the Uwharrie hills there is an unmarked grave, which, even today, no matter how often it is filled, keeps on sinking in. It is a grave that was dug for two bodies—and it got only one.

PHANTOM FAMILY OF FIVE

YOU COULD LOOK at Jubal Reeves and know that he was the happiest family man in the Uwharrie Mountains. Kindness radiated from his ruddy face. His whole body, homely and average-looking, appeared eternally poised, as if ready to leap out at you with love and a good deed. When he spoke, you could feel his gentle voice caressing your mind and heart, stirring up visions of fresh flowers, sunshiny meadows, and crackling fireplaces on cold nights. Little ones were drawn to him despite their inherent shyness.

The reason for his great happiness was his pretty wife, Rebekah, and their four children: Hannah, ten; Laban, eight; Sarah, six; and David, three.

Anything good said about Jubal could be doubled for Rebekah. The Uwharrie people called her the best young wife and mother in the hill country. Her voice could be distinguished above all the rest for its angelic tone when the congregation stood to sing in the little log church at the foot of Cedar Mountain.

Since the community had no school, Rebekah and Jubal invited the neighborhood children to their home and taught them to read and write. In return, the other families helped Jubal cut firewood and gather his crops.

Jubal tried ever harder to think of new ways of expressing his love to his family. He lugged white flint stones from the craggy hillsides to build terraced flower gardens for his wife around the modest cabin. He whittled small wooden troughs and channeled spring water into the cabin for the convenience of the family. He slung swings under the trees for the children, built them crude wagons, and whittled toys and whistles.

One year, in the snowy, icy still of winter, a mantle of gloom and fear spread over the people of the Uwharries. An epidemic of influenza raged unchecked, bringing sickness and death to practically every family. The little medicine that was available proved ineffective, and the lone country doctor could not get around nearly fast enough. Despite his valiant efforts, many of his patients died.

Rebekah ministered to the sick until she came home one evening and found her own children ailing. In spite of the precautions they had taken, all four had suddenly become ill. Little David died the next day. The other children were too sick to know. Jubal and Rebekah wept brokenly. Then Rebekah was stricken and put to bed, where she weakened quickly. But before she grew too ill to care, she knew that Hannah, her eldest child, had died there in the bed beside her.

Then, Jubal, brokenhearted and grieving, succumbed to the disease in spite of his valiant efforts to stay on his feet and care for his beloved family. He slumped over his bed, unconscious and exhausted. Neighbors found him the next day and stayed to help after sending word to the doctor. Rebekah, the loving wife and mother, had died before the doctor arrived. Sarah was the next to go. And then Laban. For a week Jubal hovered on that narrow border between life and death before his condition improved. It was another few days before he recovered sufficiently to sit up and ask about his family.

They began by telling him of the grim toll the epidemic had taken through all the country: that many families had lost one and sometimes several members. Then, as gently as they knew how, they told him that his wife and four children lay buried in new graves on a little rise of ground near the flower gardens.

From the very first, it didn't seem to register on him. They said he just stared straight at them with a queer glint in his moist blue eyes. He just sort of shook his head in disbelief.

On the advice of the doctor and the preacher, too, the neighbors decided to leave and let Jubal Reeves fight his own battle with his overwhelming burden of heartbreak and grief. No one visited him for a week or so. People passing on the wagon road near his cabin saw him going about his usual chores. In another week or two he came to Pike's General Store to purchase some supplies. He looked haggard, but apparently he had regained his strength and composure.

Several customers and loungers heard Jubal give his order to Mr. Pike. Then, as he was about to leave, Jubal said, "I almost forgot. Rebekah wants a few yards of gingham to make dresses for the girls. And I'd better take some of that stick candy for the children, too."

Every head in the store swung toward Jubal to see what ailed the man. Pike stared at Jubal while the soiled apron covering his belly pushed hard at the counter.

"You don't really want that stuff, do you, Jubal? After what's happened?"

"Sure I want it," Jubal said. "Get it up. Nothing's happened." He gave the storekeeper a puzzled look.

Intrigued by his words, people began visiting Jubal at odd times and loitering on the road around his cabin to note any peculiarities. They reported strange things.

It was plain to see that Jubal believed his dead wife and children were still with him there at the cabin, just as they had always been.

They said he washed clothes and hung them out to dry—dresses for his daughters, larger dresses for his wife, and overalls for his little sons.

He sat outside on sunny days with a book in his hands as if teaching his children to read.

A neighbor and his wife reached the cabin at suppertime one day and found Jubal eating at the head of the table. Around the table were set plates and glasses, forks and spoons, for five other people. When he washed his dishes, he washed these extra utensils though they were unused.

Friends tried to talk to him about his deceased wife and children, emphasizing that they were gone beyond recall. The preacher came and talked kindly with him. Jubal mostly listened and nodded his head. The preacher said that apparently Jubal's mind had been stunned by his tragic loss and that he would not accept the fact that his family had been wiped out and was no longer with him.

It became obvious, too, that Jubal thought his responsibilities to his family had not diminished. In his unbalanced mind, he saw his wife and four children still with him, needing him, depending on him, and returning his passionate love, which only seemed to grow greater with the years. People tried to shatter and explode this illusion and obsession. No one succeeded. Jubal just grinned and shook his head and never talked much. When they came to realize that, in the man's pathetically twisted mind, the dead members of his family were still real flesh-and-blood people, they stopped trying to dissuade him. Instead, they held a vast pity in their hearts for Jubal Reeves, the man with the phantom family of five.

Jubal became an eccentric and a recluse, seldom seen by anyone except visitors to his cabin in the mountain cove.

No longer did the children gather at the Reeves cabin to be taught. Jubal's contacts with the outside became fewer. A new road came into use in the area, leaving the Reeves cabin pretty much isolated in its mountain sanctuary. When his money ran out, Jubal sold off a few acres of timber to the sawmillers and let Mr. Pike down at the store keep the money to ration out to him. Only occasionally did some of the older people drop by the cabin to see that Jubal did not suffer hardships. Each time, they reported Jubal more strongly tied in his uncanny allegiance to his dead wife and children.

As the years crept forward, so did Jubal's devotion and concern for his phantom family. The flower beds, which his wife had loved so much, were kept tidy and fresh and were renewed each year with more and lovelier flowers. Jubal built trellises and arbors for the climbing roses and grapes. He became an intimate friend of the wild animals and birds that came to drink at his pools in the spring run. He could be seen pulling his homemade wagon around as if it were filled with happy youngsters. About once a year he walked to a neighbor woman's house with a bolt of cloth and asked that dresses be made for his wife and girls.

In the latter years, when Jubal had become an old, white-headed man with a flowing white beard, you could approach the Reeves cabin through the woods and get close enough to hear old Jubal talking and laughing with his wife and children. When asked about them, Jubal just smiled and made no comment. But folks remember that, in his last years, Jubal glowed with a keener pleasure and radiated a happiness similar to his earlier happiness before the terrible epidemic.

About dark one winter evening, a newcomer to the community, unfamiliar with the tradition of Jubal Reeves, stopped at the Reeves cabin to ask directions. He found Jubal, feeble with age, decorating his dining table with holly twigs and setting six clean plates and accessories around the table. Enough food loaded the table to feed six people amply. At four of the settings were little animals and figures and trinkets made of wood and acorns. Since it was Christmastime, the man assumed that the cabin was being prepared for the festive occasion. Jubal's eyes crinkled gaily under shaggy brows. His hair glistened, his beard was trimmed, and his clothes were neat and clean.

The stranger had business over the ridge at another cabin. On his return two hours later, he neared the Reeves cabin and decided to stop and thaw himself out by the roaring fireplace before continuing his journey home. But just as he was about to blow out his lantern light and knock on the door, the sound of many merry voices stopped him.

There came the distinct sound of gay laughter, he told the villagers later, and the lively banter of children and the delighted squeals of a young child. He heard singing by children and adults, then singing by a young woman, whose voice reminded him of nothing less than the voice of an angel.

He knew it would be grossly rude to intrude into this happy family gathering, so he turned his lantern wick higher, crept away from the cabin, and plunged into the cold woods at a quickened pace for home.

"It did, honestly," he told the older Uwharrie people later. "It sounded just like a big happy family in there celebrating, or having a party, or something."

This man was sorely troubled when they told him the living legend of Jubal Reeves and his phantom family of five.

It was late the next summer, in those few glorious days when the summer sun refuses to yield to the invigorating autumn breezes, that they found Jubal Reeves lying in his stone chair out near the flower gardens. His head rested gently against the stone, and his sightless eyes were turned toward a row of five neat graves on the little knoll above the roses. A bit of a smile was locked on his face.

A sixth grave was added to the row of graves at the old Jubal Reeves homeplace somewhere in the hills of the Uwharries. But few know where this spot is any more. Only rarely does an adventurous family prowl deep enough into the forest byways to notice the geometric patterns of white flint stones and the profusion of wild flowers carpeting the ground around a tiny bubbling spring. Only the most careful search would ever reveal the location of the six graves that have been all but obliterated by the encroaching forest.

To this day, the people of the Uwharries believe that the wife and four children of Jubal Reeves did reappear in person to the old man in his waning years to bring reality to the dream and illusion he had cherished for so long.

The name of Jubal Reeves has been kept alive in the Uwharrie country, but only the elderly appreciate its significance. The highest compliment that can be paid an individual who shows great charity and love toward his fellowmen is

"He shows a love like the love of Jubal Reeves."

THE HATCHET-SWINGING FIRE

Thaddeus, an orphaned mountain boy, had taken up residence in the old Moser cabin in a wild cove of the Uwharries, up from the Yadkin River. Not so much from a fondness for isolation as from a desire for independence, did he fix up the place enough to see him through the winter. Old man Morrison and one of his sons had helped him throw new poles across the roof, board up the holes in the walls, and repair the fallen stone chimney. He had worked for the Morrisons during the summer and fall. With his meager earnings he had bought and traded himself into possession of a long-barreled gun and a few steel traps with which he hoped to spend a profitable winter season.

Folks had warned him against it. "Won't do for you to stay up there alone all winter, son," they said. "You'll go batty when old man Moser's ghosts start prowling around."

The Morrisons and other people in the community had told him fearsome things about the Moser place. Scary tales about noises and inexplicable sights. Moser, an irascible old man of the woods, had died twenty years before, and his bones lay buried in an unmarked grave somewhere near the cabin. Since then, the unused one-room dwelling had crumbled into almost nothing, and it had taken Thad many days of labor to fortify it against the onslaughts of winter. One of his biggest jobs had been lugging a wagonload of green lumber, which had cost him a week's wages, up the hill, and flooring as much of the shack as the boards would cover.

With the boldness and ambition of a twenty-year-old, Thad had gone into the woods. He ran his traps by day and spent the nights trying to keep warm in his crude bed on the floor near the fire-place. Many of the stones in the walls and top of the fireplace had sagged out of place, which made them look like rows of teeth ready to snap and gobble him up.

The first time he noticed anything unnatural about the fire was late one winter night when he woke up and saw the flames acting strangely. The fire had died to a bed of coals in front of the back-log, as usual. Thad raised his head and watched in fascination. He was lying on the floor with his feet stretched toward the mouth of the fireplace.

He saw an orange finger of flame curl up out of the bed of coals and then dance around in the air before it lashed swiftly toward his feet. Instinctively, he jerked his feet up under the blankets toward his body. He heard and felt something strike hard amid the ends of the blankets on the floor, where his feet had been only seconds be-fore.

Twisting into a sitting position, he watched the long, menacing arm of flame sweep from side to side like a giant cobra searching for him. Occasionally the end of it fell swiftly, and he heard a thud as something struck the floor with force.

He got up, lit the candle on his table, moved to a far corner of the room, and wrapped the blankets around him. Soon the flashing flames slid back into the bed of coals. It became frightfully cold there in the corner on the half-frozen dirt floor. Too cold. The dying fire looked quite peaceful again. Thad moved his blankets back onto the floor in front of the fireplace and lay down. Warmer now, he dozed off.

Flashing light woke him. Long, jagged arms of flame were leap-ing out over him again. Quickly he rolled away from the fireplace, and as he looked back, the flames struck downward, and thuds sounded on the floor. Soon the flames receded again.

This time he shoved his slab table against the wall and, huddling in his blankets on the table, slept fitfully until dawn. Then he got up, threw kindling on the fire, and soon had a crackling blaze roaring up the chimney. Suddenly he saw it. There on the rough oak boards in front of the hearthstone were long, inch-deep imprints such as an axe or hatchet might have made. The wood around them was charred. He bent and examined the gashes closely, and his face clouded with disbelief as he recalled the experiences of the night before.

He finished with his traps early that day, walked the long trail down to the village of Tuckertown, and told the folks there about his experiences with the fire.

"Ahhh," they said. " 'Twas like we expected. You can't stay up there alone, boy. Old man Moser's ha'nts are after you. Everybody knows that place is jinxed."

But since no one offered him an alternative, the defiant young man turned back to the foreboding mountain, determined to stay out the winter in the Moser cabin, dancing fire or no.

On his way out of the village, he stopped by the clapboard home of Mary Ann, a girl of about his own age whom he had talked to a few times before. Her face blossomed into a smile like a crimson rose when she saw him. Brown hair rustled around her shoulders. Her hands untied the apron from her waist and smoothed her fresh gingham dress. Behind her, Thad saw her father come to the door and lean against it, regarding Thad with an expression of disdain saved for suitors with no means and little prospects.

An arm's length away, Thad spoke to the girl. "I'm going back up the mountain," he said awkwardly, with a sudden surge of inferiority and self-consciousness. "I won't be back till spring. I—I just thought I'd stop by and tell you I'd be back then."

She nodded. "I'm glad you did stop. I dread for you to spend the winter off up there in those terrible woods." Impulsively she unfastened the chain of a little golden locket from around her neck, pressed it into his hands, and stepped back. "Take this with you and bring it back to me in the spring."

"Mary Ann," came a rough masculine voice from the doorway, "you come on in the house."

Thad turned and waved to her once before he walked out of the yard and into the trees. The bleak December sky loosened a flurry of snowflakes as he hurried up the trail in the waning light of late afternoon.

It snowed that night and most of the next day.

Confined to the cabin, Thad kept the fireplace piled with logs, and the fire roared merrily up the chimney. During the night he made a discovery about the fire. As long as there was plenty of fuel on the fire, there was no sign of anything menacing or abnormal. But if he let it die down low, he could count on those long curling flames to rise and dance and flick out wildly and chop at the floor with an unseen tool. Mostly it occurred at night. But once Thad returned from his traps at high noon and heard hammering on the hearth boards.

Thad had a visitor a few days later, Bert Morrison, one of the boys he had worked with during the summer. Bert had heard from the villagers about the strange behavior of the fire, and he had come to see it firsthand.

"I gotta see it myself, Thad," Bert said, "before I'll believe it. I think you've been here alone so long you're seein' things that ain't there a-tall."

After a skimpy supper, the boys sat by the roaring fire and whittled and talked. Thad told Bert that, if anything should happen to him here during the winter, his belongings were to go to Mary Ann.

The warm fire lulled Bert into drowsiness, and he said that he was ready for bed. Thad spread some ragged blankets over the boards in front of the hearth, and Bert removed his heavy boots and lay down. The fire died slowly, and the light in the room grew dimmer. Pulling the blankets around him, Thad crawled on top of the table to watch and wait.

Some little time passed before Thad saw any movement in the fire. Bert snored soundly. Then the peaceful fire began its savage dance, the flames licking out viciously. Abruptly, the flames darted out into the room over Bert's body. Thad moved hurriedly to wake the boy and drag him out of danger.

But Bert's head lifted. Then he sat bolt upright, drawing up his feet. Just in time, too. The ends of the flames fell swiftly again and again. There were thuds muffled by the blankets where Bert's feet and legs had been an instant before.

For a moment, Bert sat there fascinated, a foolish look on his face, watching the wicked flames lash out over him. Thad lunged forward to drag him away. But Bert let out a terrified shriek, jumped up, and ran for the door, forgetting his boots. With a look of stark horror on his face, he was out the door before Thad could stop him.

Thad rushed to the door to look and listen. Outside, the snow lay in scattered patches under a brittle moon. A frigid wind cavorted among the tall pines and tore around the eaves of the cabin. Thad could hear Bert's wild shrieking far down the trail. There was no point in going after him. Bert knew the trail, and he wouldn't stop until he reached the village. As long as he kept running, he wouldn't freeze.

The winter passed slowly with its snow and ice and bitter cold. Oldsters reckoned it was one of the foulest winters seen in a lifetime.

It was well into the dark nights of March before the villagers began wondering when Thad would be coming down from the mountain with his winter's catch. After two consecutive afternoons of discussing it around the pot-bellied stove in the Tuckertown store, some of the younger men decided to pay Thad a neighborly visit. Maybe they could help him lug down his hides.

In the group that trudged up the mountain the next day was a grim-faced Bert Morrison. No smoke came from the old cabin as the men approached. The place looked dead. The rickety door had swelled and had to be forced open.

All the half-dozen men had filed inside the dim room before they saw it. The silence was complete, a stunned hush as the men stared with unbelieving eyes.

Scattered like scraps of rags and bark on the floor in front of the dead fireplace lay the barely recognizable pieces of a human body. It had been horribly hacked and mangled to bits.

The men backed outside, sick from the sight within the cabin. They wagged their heads and stared blankly at each other.

"Let's get away from this devilish place," one man said, retching drily. "There ain't even enough left of him to bury decent."

But Bert Morrison remembered his promise. He kept his eyes averted as he ransacked the cabin for the personal effects of his deceased friend. He dumped them into a burlap sack he found hanging from a rafter pole. Included in the sack was a little golden locket on a tiny chain.

Tuckertown was a stricken and burdened community after the news circulated late that afternoon. A tense and sad-faced young woman shed tears as she looked through the scant belongings of the young man she had hoped someday to marry.

One of the men who had visited the cabin and witnessed the grue-some sight added a final touch of horror to the story.

"I saw it plain," he told the people. "That thing in the fireplace. The fire looked dead out, like it had been out for weeks. It weren't. Not plumb out. There was one lone red firecoal glowing in the ashes on one side. I saw it plain. It looked like a mean, evil red eye, glaring at you from straight outta Hell itself!"

That fire is not dead, even to this day, the old folks in the Yadkin River hill country will tell you. Sometimes, when it is late at night, and the fire in the fireplace has begun to burn low, and there seems to be only a single coal glowing red in the darkness, an old house-wife will jump up quickly and put more wood on the fire, lest a single flame curl up from the ashes, waver in the air a moment, and then chop at you with hatchets of fire.

THE FRIENDLY HANDS

MANY YEARS AGO, beside a little road on the outskirts of Albemarle, North Carolina, there stood a huge oak tree, which was recognized as a venerable landmark. On cold winter nights the stars seemed to catch in its topmost branches and glisten there like diamonds caressed by the wind. In spring and summer, birds nested in its leafy sanctuary, and children rigged swings from its lower limbs. Travelers often rested their weary bones in its cooling shade.

Vendors began setting up business under the oak, hoping to attract the Negroes who traveled the road to and from the nearby community. The slier peddlers often took unfair advantage of their gullible customers and were gone before discovery was made and restitution demanded. Traders soon spread the word about the lucrative location, and before many years the Negroes were being bilked by a procession of vagabond merchants.

One day a huckster, who had set his display under the tree, saw his bottles of cure-all rise off the small table and drop into the dust—all by themselves. He recovered the bottles, wiped them clean, and set them back on display. They plopped into the dust once more—again all by themselves. Then, suddenly, all his merchandise slid off the table, as if someone had swept it off in one motion. He stooped to reclaim his goods and then changed his mind. He stood up and looked around, trying to figure out what was going on.

All at once he began shrieking in pain and fright. He twisted and ducked and covered his head, trying to protect himself from powerful licks that came from nowhere. Overhead, the leaves of the big oak rustled ominously. The peddler grabbed his trinkets and rushed to his wagon. Only after he was outside the shade of the tree did the blows stop. He packed his goods as fast as he could and whipped his horse into a frenzied getaway.

As different vendors came and experienced the same thing, the word circulated among the sales fraternity. Soon unscrupulous traders stopped coming to bother the people. The Negroes wondered what unseen benefactor had aided them and how and why.

Old Jethro Tate was the first to see the hands. Trudging home one night after a long day's work in the fields of a white farmer, he was wondering how he could feed and clothe his wife and children with the pittance he had made. As he passed under the big oak, something touched his elbow, steered him to the edge of the road, and pulled him down into a crouching position. And there on the rain-washed gravel, in a shaft of moonlight, Jethro saw the glint of a gold coin. Elated, he snatched it up close to his eyes. In his trembling hand he held a twenty-dollar gold piece. Dumbfounded, he looked around to thank his benefactor. But no one was there.

Suddenly it occurred to him that it had been a glowing hand, without any arm or body attached, that had led him to the gold piece. Jethro hurried home. He alternately whimpered in fright and gibbered in gratitude as he told his family and neighbors about the golden hand that had showed him the coin.

Conditions improved for Jethro after that. He gained a new self-assurance—because someone cared.

Afterward, other members of the Negro colony had similar experiences near the oak. A wagon wheel ran off its axle one dark night. The driver jacked up the axle with blocks, heaved the wheel on, and began searching for the lost pin which had held the wheel in place. A pair of glowing hands appeared, holding the desired object out to him. He took the pin, fastened it in place, and was well on his way before the import of the event struck him and set his teeth to chattering.

On another occasion, bystanders were astounded to see the pair of hands holding and administering a sound spanking to an un-disciplined boy who had been bullying a timid and frail child.

After many such experiences, it became apparent that the hands were friendly and quite helpful. They showed no favoritism or discrimination, performing equally well for the poor and for the aristocracy of the community.

The hands looked human and quite normal in the daytime. Never was any other part of a body seen. The hands followed no specific pattern or special routine. They appeared and performed whenever they were needed. But they never strayed far away from the big oak tree.

Since the hands encouraged it, the people began utilizing them for practical purposes. They knitted, quilted, mended clothes, husked roasting ear corn, shelled garden peas, and picked seeds out of cotton. They sharpened tools, adjusted and repaired machinery, trimmed lamp wicks, cleaned lantern globes, poured wax candles, molded bullets, drew house plans, and designed futuristic buildings. They bottomed chairs, molded clay, sculpted in granite, and painted pictures. There seemed to be no end to the skills they possessed.

On Sunday the hands performed no work. Passers-by could often see them clasped together as if underneath an unseen chin in the traditional pose of prayer. This led the Negro preacher to bring his flock to the shade of the oak for Sunday services. Whenever the congregation stood to sing, the hands directed the choir. The preach-er preached sermons about the helpful hands, calling on all people to respect and revere them.

Aunt Clinie Bell had never had much luck teaching herself to play the piano, the one luxury she had scrimped and saved to buy and set up in her modest home not far from the big oak. She had wanted desperately to learn to play the piano, so she could move it to the little church and play for the singing and services there where all could hear. But her fingers never attained the proper co-ordination. In a last attempt, she had some neighbors move the piano under the oak tree. As she despaired over the keyboard, a pair of golden hands appeared and began to guide her, teaching her the subtleties of position, timing, cadence, rhythm, and tone. Enthralled, Aunt Clinie Bell had the neighbors move the piano back to her house, where she practiced for hours each day. It wasn't long before she had men from the church come and move her piano into the sanctuary. The people were amazed at the way Aunt Clinie Bell's playing had improved. Inspired playing, they called it. The services in the little church now were great and fervent since her playing had rejuvenated the congregation.

Lionel Leanberry owed his life, and his career, to the hands. A group of mob-crazed men dragged him from his home in the middle of the night, bound him, and took him to the big tree to lynch. They said he had been seen and identified as fleeing from a burning house, in which fire took the life of a helpless mother and her child. So he had to pay with his life. Lionel protested his innocence, but they tightened a noose about his neck and drove a bareback mule from under him before anyone knew what was happening.

Just as the helpless man slid off the rump of the mule, a pair of golden hands materialized. One hand grabbed his clothing and supported him, while the other hand broke the rope. In front of the speechless crowd, the hands untied the ropes and deposited Lionel gently on the ground. Then the hands moved slowly through the mob and stopped over a quaking Negro man. The hands grabbed him around the neck, lifted him, kicking and squalling, off the ground, carried him to the mule, and dropped him roughly on the mule's back. They pulled down the broken rope from the tree limb and bound his hands behind him, then began fashioning an expert hangman's noose in front of the Negro's face.

He could stand it no longer. "I done it! I done it! Lionel didn't do it—I did!" he screamed. "Git these devil hands away from me. Do what you wants to, but git these things away from heah. Cain't we wait till mornin'? We is all crazy dreamin'. Lawdy . . . Lawdy!"

The Friendly Hands   25

When the Negro confessed, the hands put down the rope, and the crowd led the man to the local jail to await trial.

Saved from a wrongful death, Lionel went up North to study, and he became a successful businessman and died rich.

Bo Caswell operated a blacksmith shop a few yards from the big oak. Young boys often stood around watching him work, and it bothered him to have them idle. He wished that he, or someone, had time to teach these boys the trade. One day, a pair of hands held a hammer handle out to a startled youth, who clasped it and found himself pulled into the shop. Other youths were similarly recruited. There was plenty of room in the shop for the hands to teach the boys blacksmithing while Bo worked at his regular trade. Anything Bo could do, the hands could do better. Often he caught himself standing idle, fascinated by the skilled hands. Anxious to learn now, the boys applied themselves to their tasks. From the apprenticeship of the hands and the shop went a series of skilled craftsmen, not only blacksmiths, but wagon-builders, furniture-makers, mill-wrights, mechanics, and woodcarvers.

Bo noticed that sometimes, when all the students were busy, the hands would go off by themselves to one end of a workbench and work on a block of wood with the carving tools. Gradually an object took shape. It looked like half a miniature hog—a fat old sow —divided lengthwise right down the middle. But it was only the top half—half the snout, the eyes and ears, and the rounded back, ending in a curly tail that would swivel. Hollow on the inside, and about a foot long, it was a work of art. The bottom edges on each side were serrated as if designed to fit into a similar pattern, though the bottom half was missing and there was never any sign of the legs and belly and jowls of the wooden sow. Bo often pondered the matter.

The versatile hands befriended a generation or two of the people of the community, always helping the deserving and the needy, often with resulting improvement in the lives of the recipients.

Then the hands became enfeebled and slow and fumbling—just as the hands of a real flesh-and-blood person lose their dexterity with advancing age. In their last years, the hands appeared less frequently, and they grew reluctant to accept tedious tasks.

Inevitably, the old oak tree was split asunder by lightning one summer night. It died slowly and stood there, a dead sentinel by the roadside, until it finally decayed into a bleached hollow shaft of weathered wood. This, too, fell when the city widened and paved the road many years ago.

One last recorded episode involving the hands occurred several decades later.

A young Negro man, walking home late one star-spangled winter night, passed by the place where the old oak had once stood. He was cursing and swearing in a loud voice. A friend had failed to keep his promise to come by to pick him up and drive him home. So, well-fortified against the cold by a drink from his host's bottle, he had set out walking. The more he walked, the more his resentment for his unpunctual friend flared inside him, until he filled the night air with purplish oaths.

"Somethin' made me look around," he told friends later, "an' I seed dis big, bright, shiny pair of hands comin' from above and reachin' out for me. Dey close around my throat and cut off my breath. I tries to holler, but I cain't. I tries to run, but my feet won't take me. Den dese fingers feel lak dey burn my neck through as dey choke my windpipe tighter an' tighter. An' de next thing I knows, I's layin' on de ground a-gettin' my senses back, a-fightin' for breath, and a-prayin' dat dem hands don't come back no mo'."

Could it be that a certain sector of road where the old oak once stood on the outskirts of Albemarle is still guarded by the ghost with the friendly hands? Or that a new edition of that ghost protects each new generation?

Bo Caswell thought so till the day he died. Bo's shop has long since vanished, and his possessions have passed into the hands of a son. Young Caswell remembers a tale his father often told of the mysterious top half of a foot-long sow which the hands had carved —one of the old man's most prized possessions as long as he lived.

One day, Junius Joyner, a young Negro, stopped by the younger Caswell's home. When he saw the top half of the wooden sow lying on a shelf, he was fascinated by the oddity.

"I've seen the bottom half of that hog somewhere. I know I have!" he exclaimed. "But where, where was it? Maybe it was . . . yeah, yeah . . . Uncle Calvin's trunk! Up in Ma's attic. He was her great-uncle. He carved that thing before he went off to war."

The visitor told the story about Uncle Calvin Trader, killed as a youth in the Civil War. Calvin, a brilliant young man with many talents, insisted on going into battle with his young white master. In a skirmish, the white soldier was killed, and Calvin was slightly wounded and taken prisoner after he had grabbed his master's weapon and killed at least one of the enemy soldiers. The Union Army branded him a murderer and sentenced him to die before a firing squad. But before they executed him, the detachment ironically stopped in the slave's own community, where they tortured him by burning off both his hands. Then they shot him.

They burned off his hands in a smithy's red-hot forge. It could have happened right there in the shop of Bo's predecessor.

The two men lost no time in comparing the two halves of the wooden sow.

In Mrs. Joyner's attic, they unlocked a molded, rusty, creaking trunk, full of Uncle Calvin's belongings and other family heirlooms. They rummaged in the bottom until they found a piece of wood with legs on it. The moldy but sturdy object was the lower half of a fat wooden sow, about a foot long. Expertly carved, it had the lower half of a snout, wrinkled jowls, knobby-kneed legs ending in distinctive pig hooves, a scaly belly full of teats, and a rear end exactly like a sow who has had one litter and is expecting another.

Caswell wiped grime from the serrated edges of the lower half's hollow belly. Slowly he lowered his top half onto it. The pieces fitted perfectly. Hardly a crack or a ripple was visible to the eye or discernible to the fingers, so intimately did the two parts embrace each other.

He discovered a ring on the end of the lower snout which flipped up and snapped over the upper snout to lock it in place. Likewise, the swiveled curly tail on the upper half had been designed to snap into the lower half's natural crevice to hold that end firmly in place.

"So that was it!" Bo's son said. "He was a natural-born teacher. His burned-off hands came back here as a ghost to finish that carving he had started while alive, and while the hands were here, they just had to teach and help other people, too."

HALF A PIECE OF GOLD

THE BITING WIND of a late winter afternoon cut at the man and woman huddled together at the front of a two-horse wagon that rattled and clanked over a rough road through the Uwharrie hills. On the woman's cold-stiffened face was a plea for her husband to stop for the night and find shelter in this strange and unfriendly land.

Great as her discomfort was, her main concern was for the little bundle of life held tightly in her arms. She pulled back the thick wraps and gently pinched the cheek of her months-old baby. It whimpered and then cried hungrily until she clutched it again to her breast.

"Please, John," she begged. "We can't stand much more of this. We must stop and find shelter. We've all got to have food and warmth."

Desperation blazed in John's eyes. "We'll do it right away," he promised. But his voice was empty of assurance.

Already they had stopped at two farmhouses and had been refused lodging for the night, even in barns or outbuildings. Bitterness over the hostility of this land filled John as his eyes sought what lay around the next bend. He studied the clouds darkening the east.

Twilight had deepened into gloom when they came upon a ramshackle two-story frame house by the road. Gaping holes yawned where its doors and windows should have been. Half the roof had tumbled in under the weight of the fallen stone chimney. An alarmed owl winged out the front door as they approached.

John unhitched the horses, put them in the nearby barn, and gave them a ration of grain. Then he took his wife and baby inside the old house and tried to make them comfortable. In the last of the fading light, he examined the stone fireplace and found it serviceable enough for a fire. He scraped together timbers and a pile of debris for fuel.

Then, to his overwhelming dismay, he discovered that he had no matches with which to ignite the kindling.

Frantically he searched his pockets again. He found no matches anywhere. There was no way even to light the stub of a candle or the coal-oil lantern they had brought into the house. When John told his wife, his voice broke. Flitting into his mind were thoughts of death by freezing in this old house, through which the wind howled and into which snowflakes were beginning to fall.

"Oh, John, you must do *something*," his wife pleaded, her eyes filling with tears. "Do something before we all die in this awful place."

John went back outside to look around. He saw a faint glimmer of light far off across the night. A farmhouse. It must have been a mile away. He could get matches there. He went back inside and found a place out of the wind and snow for his wife and child. Thoughts of vicious timber wolves prowling around the old house made him hesitate. His wife and the baby would be at their mercy, for her fingers were too numb to operate the old muzzle-loader he would leave by her side. Yet, she was too exhausted to attempt walking over the rough terrain to the lighted farmhouse—where they might be refused help anyway. No, he would hurry there alone, get the matches, and return before the wolves had a chance to stalk. He wrapped another quilt around her feet. Then he set out on foot for the glimmering light far across the valley.

It took him almost an hour, stumbling through the snowy fields and thickets, to reach the farmhouse. A shriveled little man in overalls, who had a cob pipe jutting out of his mouth, received him into a room lighted by a crackling fire, where John warmed his nearly frozen body. When he explained his predicament and his mission to the farmer, the face of his host paled, and his bushy-browed eyes widened.

"You can't go back there tonight," he declared. "You'll be ripped to pieces. Lots of people have been killed there. That house is ha'nted. Wayfarers have stopped there to spend the night, and the next mornin' all that's left of them is little piles of bones. I've seed it. Your wife and child are dead by now. You'll die, too, if you go back there. Stay here with us till mornin', and then we'll all go back and take a look."

John protested, "But, but . . . they're waiting on me . . . depending on me. . . . They'll freeze. . . . They're expecting me. . . . I've gotta go back. . . ."

With surprising strength, the farmer thrust him into a big rocker and tied his hands and feet to the chair.

Back at the house, the woman wept quietly in the darkness. In her heart she felt that her husband wasn't coming back. Maybe he had lost his way and was freezing to death out there in the drifting snow. Or maybe, in cowardice and fear, he had abandoned them.

To her ears came a sound—*clump-thump-ump*—steps on the broken stairs that rose into the blackness across the room. The sound drew nearer. Then into her sight came a ghastly apparition that froze her into speechless immobility. All she could do was stare in horror.

She saw a yellow glow outlining the upper part of a man's body. The lolling head, with a bony face and gleaming eyes, lay back at a sharp angle. An ugly slash stretched across the throat from ear to ear.

The apparition glided menacingly toward the woman as she clung to her baby.

Terrified as she was, the woman remembered that, to pacify a supernatural being, one must address it by repeating the three highest words in the Bible. Just before the thing reached her, she blurted out, in quivering notes, the names of the Trinity. The figure stopped.

"I'm so glad you said that," a cadaverous voice croaked, "for in another instant you and your baby would have been bits of bone scattered over the floor . . . like so many others have been. For many long years I've waited for someone to speak those words and unlock my secret."

The ghostly figure bent and touched a finger to the dead wick in the lantern. A dim light fluttered over the room as the wick flamed.

"You will not be harmed," he said. "Bring the light and follow me. I will show you something that will make you rich."

He turned and moved to the outside door. The trembling woman clasped her baby in one arm, picked up the lantern, and followed him. They went outside into the wind and snow, around the end of the house, and down a slippery bank into a crude, damp cellar.

At the far side, the apparition stopped.

"Dig here," he said, indicating a spot in the black earth. He motioned to a rusty mattock leaning against the wall.

The woman saw a wooden box, found that it was empty, and placed her well-wrapped baby inside. Then she lifted the rusty mattock and drove it into the earth, raking back the loosened dirt. Presently the tool struck a rock.

"Scrape back the earth and lift the rock," ordered the apparition. The woman did so.

And there, lying exposed in the hole at her feet, was a large iron pot filled to the brim with gold pieces. The dull luster of the golden heap glistened in the feeble lantern light.

"I was murdered because of this," the glowing figure said. "But no one ever found it. People have come here to look for it, and I've had to destroy them. I've been hoping for years that someone would say the words you said, so I could reveal the gold to him and get him to help me. There's something I want you to do for me now."

The ghastly head turned to her commandingly.

"I have a brother, name of Travis, still living near here. He was

Half a Piece of Gold   33

always good to me. Anybody can tell you where he lives. I want you to take this gold and count it and divide it exactly in half. You can keep one half. Give the other half to my brother."

He paused, then continued.

"Remember to divide it exactly in half. If there is one odd piece left over, cut it through the middle, and each take one half."

They went back out of the cellar and into the house.

"I can go away from here with relief, now that I know the money is taken care of," the murdered man said. "You can never imagine what torment I've gone through since I was killed, just worrying about that money. I will never bother anyone here again."

He turned as if to leave.

"Wait!" cried the woman. "I want to thank you before you go." She started toward him, her hand extended.

"Stop!" he commanded. She halted, surprised.

"You mustn't touch me or you will be harmed. I'll show you what I mean."

He reached out and touched the corner of her apron, and the garment became scorched and charred, in the pattern of fingerprints.

She looked at it, stunned. Then, hopefully, she blurted, "But . . . the fireplace . . . ."

The glowing apparition, its throat-cut head dangling and bobbing on its shoulders, moved to the fireplace and touched a finger to the kindling. Instantly fire licked cheerily up the chimney.

"Maybe that will make my torment in Hell a little less severe," the figure said. And it was gone.

Next day, the midmorning sun tried to find a hole in the shifting clouds as John and the farmer crunched through the snow to the old house. They entered apprehensively, fearful of what they would find. But they saw the woman and the baby fairly comfortable before a roaring fire. The woman had found more wood for the fire and had brought in food from the wagon.

John clasped her, sobbing his relief.

Composed and apparently refreshed, his wife told John and the farmer about her experience of the night. She showed them the apron with the scorched fingerprints.

The two men went to the cellar and brought back the pot of gold pieces. The farmer located the murdered man's brother. Later they counted the gold pieces and divided them.

There was one odd piece. This they cut precisely down the middle, and each took half.

With their share of the gold, John and his wife bought a house and settled down in that community in the Uwharries. There was one half piece of gold left over. John and his wife kept it and had a long and happy life together. They were never again visited by a ghost.

Therein was born a superstition. Even today, it's considered a good omen by people in the Uwharries to have in one's personal possession one half of a gold coin which has been cut exactly down the middle. They say it keeps evil away.

A BARGAIN WITH THE DEVIL

To REWARD DIVES for his long years of hard work as the village blacksmith, the Good Fairy appeared to him in his shop one day and gave him three wishes.

Dives thought for a while, and then he said, "That hammer over there. Whenever I want to use it, someone else always has it. No one ever returns it to its proper place. So, I wish that whoever picks up that hammer won't be able to turn it loose until I say so. Maybe that will teach him a lesson."

The Good Fairy nodded.

"The same thing happens with my old rocking chair at home," Dives continued. "When I go home at the end of the day, tired and in need of solace, someone else is always in my rocker, depriving me of my rest. So, I wish that whoever sits down in my rocking chair won't be able to get out until I say so."

Again the Good Fairy nodded.

Dives contemplated his third and final wish.

"My money has an irksome habit of flying out of my purse, and I have trouble keeping any there. So, I wish that any money I put in my purse will stay there until I tell it to come out."

"Granted," said the Good Fairy. "So it shall be."

Years passed, and one day Satan appeared in the shop, informing Dives that he had come to take him to Hell.

Dives said okay, he reckoned he'd go peaceably if only Satan would let him finish this one plow shovel he was now sharpening. Would Satan hand him that short-handled four-pound hammer over there so he could use it to get the work completed more quickly?

Eager to be off with his victim, Satan grabbed the hammer to hand to Dives. But he discovered that he could not let it go. In a fit of rage, he whirled around the shop; but nothing he did made the cumbersome tool drop.

Dives laughed. "That hammer will not leave your hand until I tell it to. So I have you trapped, Satan, ol' boy. You're *my* prisoner now."

Satan began to bargain and plead. "I'll go away and not bother you again for twenty years if you'll free me of this detestable thing," he promised.

To Dives, twenty more years looked enticing, so he agreed. At his bidding, the hammer dropped from Satan's hand, and Satan went away.

At the end of twenty years Satan returned and vindictively commanded that Dives come with him quickly, without any tricks. Dives reluctantly agreed, asking only that he be allowed to leave the shop and go by his home to clean up a bit before departing on the journey to that Awful Place. Once inside his house, Dives motioned Satan toward an inviting rocking chair.

"Sit down here and make yourself comfortable while I wash off the grime and change clothes. I'll only be a few minutes."

Satan sat down in the rocker, and before long he discovered that he could not get out of it. He roared and stamped his feet and waved his arms and heaved mightily, but he could not budge from the rocking chair.

"That chair will not release you until I so bid it," Dives gloated. "So now you are my prisoner again."

Satan squirmed and bargained. In exchange for his freedom, Satan promised Dives twenty more years without molestation. Already an old man, Dives found this offer highly attractive, so he agreed to the terms and directed the chair to free Satan, who straightway disappeared.

When twenty more years had passed, Satan reappeared right on schedule. He bade Dives come along quickly and gave him no chance to resort to trickery. By this time Dives was a feeble old man. He said he had lived longer than his allotted time anyway, so he'd come along without further ado. They started walking down the lonesome road.

It happened to be a sultry summer day. The sun burned upon the dusty road over which they trudged. Dives faltered as he pulled his collar loose and wiped perspiration from his brow. The Devil, too, appeared to wilt and cringe in the intense midday heat and light.

"Ah-hhh," the Devil said, "a cool drink would be ever so enjoyable right now."

Dives spoke:

"Mister Devil, they say you can assume any form or shape that suits you. There's a country store up ahead. Turn yourself into a dime, and I'll put you into my purse, and when we get to the store I'll go inside and buy us a cool drink each. It will be my last one. I'll bring our drinks back outside and wait while you change yourself into a gnat. Then you can fly through a crack in the door to join me, and we can resume our journey refreshed."

The idea appealed to Satan. So he changed himself into a thin dime in Dives' palm. Quickly, Dives put the dime deep inside his purse and returned the purse to his pocket.

"Now I've got you fast again, and I'll never let you go," he cried triumphantly.

Unable to talk or communicate or even move in his inanimate condition, Satan had no way of escaping from his predicament. And Dives wasn't about to free him.

Some time later, Dives died a natural death.

Heaven would not receive him because he had Satan in his pocket. Nor would Hell because its proprietor was absent.

So Dives' soul was consigned to an eternity of lonely wandering. It was turned into a glowing Jack-o'-Lantern that assumes various ghostly shapes, one of which is a phosphorescent mass of light often seen hovering mysteriously around the woods and swamps in the Uwharries.

A Bargain with the Devil   39

THE MIDNIGHT HUNTER

A HOLLOW *knock-knock-knock* shook the door of the Poker Thompson cabin on Machine Branch at the stroke of twelve on an early winter night. Inside, the Thompsons slept soundly under heavy quilts. Outside, a vicious wind tormented the tree branches, which danced in frenzy under a mantle of pale moonlight. It was not the kind of night on which you would expect visitors to come knocking on your door.

A second sharp rapping roused Poker Thompson. Sleepily he struggled out of his bed, threw an old coat around his shoulders, and padded to the door in his stocking feet. He unbolted the door and looked from right to left. He saw no one. Then his eyes focused on a white shape resembling a man, receding across the far side of the yard and into the edge of the forest.

What was it? He decided it looked too white to be a person. And it glided along too smoothly to be a man walking. It appeared to be slim and bony. Bony? That was it, Poker Thompson realized. Sudden apprehension chilled his blood more intensely than did the frigid air.

The thing fading into the shadows of the woods looked like a bunch of bleached bones hung together in human shape. Just prior to disappearing into the gloom, a bony arm motioned a time or two as though it wanted him to follow.

Before he could budge from his tracks, Thompson felt the hair on the back of his neck rise at another sound—the lonely, unearthly baying of a hound dog that had treed a coon in the deep woods over across the valley.

Slamming and bolting the door, Thompson ran wildly back to his room, shouting for his wife Mandy.

While Poker Thompson's family tried to listen patiently to his chatter about the apparition and to calm his nervous excitement, two other residents of the community, one a middle-aged farmer and the other a sixteen-year-old boy, experienced similar visitations. Each reported that a ghostly object had summoned him to the door, retreated, beckoned him to follow, and then vanished. Their descriptions coincided pretty well with Poker Thompson's, except that the boy called the thing a skeleton.

When their stories had circulated around the Uwharrie hills, people reacted with ridicule and skepticism, even after the three sighters met and corroborated each others' accounts. Soon, however, the trio had reinforcements, other converts who shakily reported their encounters with the mysterious midnight caller.

Gradually, from the growing list of witnesses, a pattern of the midnight ghost's behavior began to emerge. The ghost appeared only at the homes of good woodsmen and hunters, preferably coon-hunters.

Sometimes the visits were made on beastly nights in the foulest weather. No rain, sleet, snow, or bitter wind deterred the ghost. Of course, it liked moonlight nights, too, as well as solid-cold, frost-smitten ones. But it preferred mist-dampened nights that made the coon scent easier for the hounds to pick up and follow.

Various reports got out that the apparition was a bleached human skeleton whose jawbones worked in soundless monologue as if it were trying to talk. Some said it carried a pine torch in its hand, or sometimes a rusty lantern, with the wire handle over a bone-white arm. Across its shoulder blade, some said, was slung a gunny sack and an axe, completing its coon-hunting gear. But every witness confirmed the bony arm rising and motioning him to follow as it vanished into the trees.

From all these observations the people deduced that the midnight skeleton was a hunter, or the ghost of a hunter, coming around to solicit companions for a coon-hunting trip into the big woods.

Poker Thompson knew of only one coon-hunter that it possibly could be. A great many years before, there had lived in the community an old man by the name of Ferdinand Crisco, a gaunt, wizened oldster with shaggy white hair and a long white beard which hung almost to his waist. The beard would have hung lower, folks said, if he hadn't kept a knot tied in the tip end of it. The knot anchored it in a breeze and kept it out of his way. "Coon" Crisco had a passion, an obsession, for coon-hunting. During the season he slept in the daytime and hunted coons at night. His preoccupation with coon-hunting had caused his family to leave him, and for decades he had lived alone in a shack at the edge of the big woods with his pack of hounds. He had one special favorite hound that he called "Old Scatter."

Never did the temperature drop too low or the ice get too slippery or the snow too deep or the wind too strong for "Coon" Crisco to go hunting. About the time most people were going to bed, Crisco and Old Scatter would hit the woods for a night of coon-chasing. Whenever he could beg enough fuel for his lantern, he would hook it over his arm to light his way in the black woods. At other times he depended on the open flame of a long pine torch. Anyone who happened to be up between midnight and dawn and glimpsed a light bobbing in and around the big woods could be sure it was Crisco, the coon-hunter.

When Old Scatter treed a coon, his excited baying was heard and recognized all over the valley. Nobody hunted with Crisco. He climbed his trees and claimed his quarry in solitude. Sometimes his rambling hunts carried him many miles away, and he would camp out in the woods for a week or longer, despite the severe weather. Other hunters would find the ashes of his campfires in the snow and come across the pine-bough shelters he erected and used from year to year.

The Midnight Hunter 43

"Tougher than a pine knot," the neighbors claimed. "He has to be to take that punishment he puts on hisself."

Early one winter Crisco failed to return from a hunt. After two weeks had passed with no sign of him, his neighbors began to express some concern. They visited his shack every day and fed the hungry hounds which had been left behind. At the end of another week, they decided to search the woods. A dozen men prowled the big woods for most of one day without turning up a trace of him in any of his old haunts. They assumed that his coon-hunting zeal had taken him far out of the community. Gradually, in the weeks that followed, the people put Crisco out of their minds.

Poker Thompson knew that the midnight ghost could be none other than the ghost of old Ferdinand Crisco, who had vanished so mysteriously years ago. But why? Why was it coming back? What did it want here now, after so much time had passed? The only way to find out was to follow it into the woods. And follow it he would, he vowed, though his family shrieked and tried to discourage him when he revealed his plan.

"Yep, I'm a-goin', I am," he declared. "I'll find out what it is ol' man 'Coon' is a-wantin' us to know. The very next night he comes around to call on me, I'll be ready to go into the woods huntin' with him and Old Scatter. We'll see."

One bitterly cold and windy night in March, the ghost knocked on his bedroom window. Poker Thompson jerked on heavy clothing and boots, grabbed his lantern, and dashed outside to see the skeleton beckoning as it vanished into the trees across the yard. He followed. The skeleton drifted along several yards in front, without regard to the trees. And now the trees thickened as the trail led through a deep pocket of the big woods.

Poker Thompson trudged bravely along with his lantern held high. Suddenly, above the moaning of the wind, he heard a sound that caused him to stop and stand motionless in the ankle-deep leaves.

The sound, a creaking, clanking noise, came again. Apparently it came not from the apparition, which seemed to have vanished, but from somewhere above him.

Poker Thompson stood under an oak tree that was of average forest girth and had many limbs. Unable to spot the origin of the sound, he held the lantern up and looked around, but its feeble glow penetrated only a few feet. Fortunately, bright moonlight bathed the tops of the trees, so he maneuvered below until he got most of the tree branches silhouetted against the moon.

Then his eyes riveted on something in the tree which tore wild gasps from his lips and started a hammer pounding in his chest.

Framed there in the moonlight, about three times as high as his head, was a human skeleton swaying slightly in the wind. Hanging from one bent elbow was a rusty lantern which squeaked and clanked as it bumped against the tree.

Panic gripped Thompson right down to his toes and brought a sound—half-yell and half-scream—tearing from his throat. He stumbled backward, lost his balance, and sat down in the leaves, his eyes never leaving that thing in the tree. Fear activated his feet, and he scrambled up and ran out of the big woods, falling and injuring himself in his haste.

He went by several homes and roused the menfolk, telling them what he had found. They decided to wait until morning before rounding up a group to go back into the woods.

More than thirty men and boys arrived at the tree early the next morning carrying ropes, a makeshift ladder, and shovels for the grim task they would have to perform. All were unnerved by the thing they saw up in the tree, a bunch of bones, rags, and mummified flesh which hung there as though life still held it together.

Then from the ground underfoot came another discovery. A man knelt and carefully raked the leaves away from the skeleton of a dog. Picked clean of flesh by buzzards and bleached dull gray by the elements, the dog's skeleton, a symmetrical cage of bones and buckled legs, lay with its head toward the tree.

"Old Scatter, sho' as you's boan," a man said, as he dropped to his knees behind the dog's bones and sighted toward the tree.

"He lay here and starved to death waiting for ol' man Crisco to come down outta that tree," said another man.

"Yeah, and his master was dead all the time," another said. "Old Scatter must have laid here for days and weeks till he weakened and died."

Death had been quicker for Crisco, they decided, as they watched two men climb the creaky ladder up into the tree where the remains decorated the bare limbs. The skeleton was supported partly by a short, jagged branch under the collarbone and partly by a taut length of dirty white beard tangled in some dried skin still fastened around the open jawbones. Although unable to understand what held the skeleton intact, they were at least able to determine the cause of the tragedy. The beard ran through a split in the base of a large, dead limb, which apparently had half-broken under its own weight. The knot on the end had locked the beard in place and had prevented it from slipping back through the crack.

In their minds they could picture old Ferdinand as he climbed jubilantly up the tree to seize the coon Old Scatter had treed. While he paused on a branch, the wind had probably whipped his long beard into the crack of the limb, unnoticed by the man. Then he had lost his footing and had hung there by his beard. Perhaps the sudden jerk had snapped his neck, or had caused unconsciousness. Maybe he had slowly strangled to death. Or maybe he had swung there in agony for hours, wailing and shouting for help until exhaustion and death stilled him, while below, Old Scatter, held there by loyalty, whimpered at his master's distress. The flame of the lantern had burned up the fuel and consumed the wick, then flickered out.

And there in the tree Crisco had remained, undisturbed, until Old Scatter became too weak to bark and frighten the buzzards away.

"Well, let's git him down so we can go," a man on the ground said to the men in the tree.

One of the men started to disengage the skeleton from its resting place and lower it to the ground. But at his touch, the skeleton disintegrated. Dozens of bones parted and dropped, bouncing off lower limbs and raining down on the crowd below, causing the men to cover their heads and dart aside. The men in the tree were so astonished by the collapse of the skeleton that they almost fell out of the tree themselves.

They gathered up the bones and wrapped them in a blanket. Someone dumped Old Scatter's bones in a gunny sack. Back out of the woods they came. After conferring with the circuit preacher, they buried the bones of Ferdinand Crisco and Old Scatter in a common grave in a corner of the old graveyard in a field near the Crisco cabin. On a tall slab of slate, which they erected at the head of the grave, someone scratched the words: "Ferdinand Crisco and his dog Old Scatter."

And there, for years, his bones lay in peace until, as Poker Thompson put it recently, the hunting urge became so overpowering that he just had to get up out of that grave and go coon-hunting again to help thin out the scandalous overpopulation of coons built up in the Uwharries during his long absence from the big woods.

"It's him again," Poker Thompson said recently when there was a strange knocking on his door at night. "Can't be nobody else. The only way to satisfy him is for someone to go with him when he comes around, but I ain't goin' again. This time it ain't *his* remains he wants to take us to. We've already found his. . . ."

THE GHOST BY THE
APPLE TREE

AUNT CAROLINE'S MIND snapped under the shock of returning from
a short visit and finding that the home of her white mistress had
burned to the ground and that the mistress and her baby son had
perished inside it. A pillaging Union army unit had cut a swath
of quick destruction and plunder through the community, then
forged southward. Aunt Caroline's duty had been explicitly assigned to her by Lieutenant Samuel Lehigh a year before, when
he left the Uwharries to serve with General Robert E. Lee. She
was to look out for the safety and well-being of the family until
his return. But he had fallen at Gettysburg, which only increased
her responsibility toward his widow and child.

Fortunately, just prior to the beginning of the war, an older
child, a daughter, had been sent to Europe to live with her father's
relatives until the bitter conflict at home was over. She, at least,
had escaped a fiery death.

The elderly slave woman helped the white neighbors bury the
remains of Mrs. Lehigh and the infant in the family plot. She
stood for hours staring at the graves and at the blackened ruins of
the dwelling. Had she been at home, this tragedy might not have
happened. She might have warned them in time to run and hide
from the invaders. But she had failed.

Shame, guilt, and grief drove her to heartbreak. Then her mind
deteriorated quickly. She lost all ability to reason.

From her shack across the wagon road from the former Lehigh

home, she began visiting the nearest neighbors, banging on their doors and windows, often late at night, always with the same pitiful plea: "My marstuh and my missus and de chillun is gone, and I can't find 'em nowhere. Please hep me find 'em. Dey has gotta come back. Dey must come back. Somethin' dependin' on 'em. Please hep me."

Poor, pathetic, mixed-up old Aunt Caroline. Still loyal, even in her insanity, to the master's family she had served for forty years. Even the most patient and kindly explanation failed to make her understand that the Lehighs were gone forever and that she might as well give up her quest. She kept at it, bothering people until she became a nuisance. She kept vigil at the graves. She sang and chanted and hummed as she puttered around the outside of her shack, giving careful attention to the new shrubs and sprouts she had set out in the soil near a large old apple tree.

The frequency of her unscheduled visits increased, as did the insistency of her plea for help in finding her lost family. She grew wild and agitated and troubled and violent. People began avoiding her and refusing to respond to her nocturnal rantings around their homes.

One morning passers-by saw the body of Aunt Caroline swinging by the neck from a plowline tied to the limb of the old apple tree. Dead for hours, she had apparently stood on a rain barrel and kicked it away, almost crushing a spindly new apple sprout rising from the loose earth. They buried her a little apart from the Lehigh woman and baby, and someone erected a crude slate headstone and scratched her name on it.

Some years passed before anyone saw Aunt Caroline again. Then, a lot of people began to see her with some degree of regularity.

Occasionally she would rattle someone's window or bang on his door, and he would come out with a lamp and see ragged old Aunt Caroline standing there, her mouth forming soundless words, a look of urgency in her eyes. At any time, day or night, she might

The Ghost by the Apple Tree   49

be seen wandering near the shack or puttering around the old orchard. Some people claimed they could even hear her singing and chanting. She was also seen keeping vigil at the Lehigh graves. For a generation or so, the ghost of Aunt Caroline became an accepted part of the community, though an enigma to natives and strangers alike.

In the midst of World War I there arrived in the community a tastefully-dressed, dignified, middle-aged woman by the name of Mrs. Kettering, who said she was the former Lillian Lehigh, the daughter who had been sent as a child to Europe to escape the ravages of the Civil War. Wartime conditions in Europe had caused the government to take over the business of the relatives with whom she had been living. Her husband had been killed early in the war, and her home had been confiscated. Her finances had dwindled. Economic conditions had driven her back to America to see what resources remained in the estate of her parents. There had been spasmodic correspondence with distant relatives here, the taxes had been paid, and the property had remained intact. Immediately upon arriving, she began taking inventory and appraising the timber and water resources, the arable and pasturable acreage, the road frontage, and so on.

One morning she paused near the site of her old home and looked at the graves of her mother and baby brother. She felt eyes upon her. Not far away, at another grave, she saw an old Negro woman in drab clothing scrutinizing her. The old woman's hands and arms moved is if she were fastening something around her neck. Then she kicked at the ground with a foot.

The aged colored woman looked vaguely familiar. Mrs. Kettering's mind flicked back half a century to her girlhood and the colored people she had known. There was one particular old woman. . . . Then she knew. Aunt Caroline! Though a lifetime had passed since she had seen her, it was she, unmistakably she. Aunt Caroline.

But could it be? Aunt Caroline had been an old woman even

back then. Could she possibly have survived? It would make her how old? Goodness. At least 110 or 115 or so. Incredible. Yet, there she stood, not ten yards away.

Elated at this new contact with her former life and at the precious knowledge it would open, Mrs. Kettering strode forward, but the hem of her dress snagged on a bush, and her attention was distracted a moment as she bent down to free her clothing. When she straightened and looked back, the Negro woman was gone.

She hurried to the spot, kicked down the weeds and vines, and dropped to her knees before a leaning, weatherworn slab of slate. She rubbed away the grime until she made out Aunt Caroline's name.

Shocked at the significance of this revelation, she sank to the ground and frantically looked around her again.

"But why, why, why?" the stunned woman breathed aloud. "Come back, Aunt Caroline. Please come back. You're my only link with the past. There must be something. What are you trying to tell me? What is it?"

Later she heard from neighbors the story of Aunt Caroline's tragic death and the events preceding and following it. The movement of her hands around her neck?

"We figger she's just going through the motions of the time she put the rope around her neck and hung herself," a farmer drawled. "But you, now. You're family. You mean more to her. She may act different to you."

The ghost of Aunt Caroline did act differently. The ghost appeared more often and at new places to this strange woman from across the sea. Always before she vanished, her hands fastened something around her neck, and a foot kicked the earth. Never did she speak, though Mrs. Kettering sometimes got the impression of faint singing or music associated with the appearances, as she did once when dreaming about the old woman. But there was no other clue to the significance of the visits. Though an educated woman, Mrs. Kettering could not fathom the ghost's purpose.

Practically penniless when she arrived, Mrs. Kettering negotiated the sale of some timber and engaged local workmen to build her a modest cottage. She chose a site amid the broom sedge and scraggly orchard trees not far from her old home. It was the place where Aunt Caroline had lived and died.

"Yup, many a time after she died, I've passed the road and seen her frittering around here," one of the elderly workmen said. "Just as natural as when she was living. Sometimes she'd be singing, too. Most always she'd be close by the old apple tree that used to stand right here where this house is going to be."

On the morning they began excavating the cellar that Mrs. Kettering wanted under the house, Aunt Caroline appeared and watched for a few minutes. All of them saw her. She made the customary motions with her hands and feet before vanishing.

After a while one of the workmen called Mrs. Kettering to the excavation. Their mule-drawn scoop had struck a metal strongbox and pulled it out of the earth. It was rusty and decaying and locked, but they could force it open with bars. Did she want them to? She told them to open it.

Pressure from the wrecking bars soon snapped the lock on the strongbox, and they threw back the lid. There was a collective gasp. A heap of gold coins glinted in the sunlight. In addition, there were several pouches. These were emptied at the woman's direction. From inside came at least two dozen necklaces—of rubies, sapphires, emeralds, opals, diamonds, and other precious stones. Most were attached to fragile golden chains.

"The Lehigh family jewels!" gasped Mrs. Kettering. "It must be! It's got to be! They are worth a fortune. I've often heard about them from the family in Europe. They have been lost for a century, and all attempts to trace them or find them have failed. Now I can see why. My father had them here with him in America, along with his own personal valuables."

The elderly workman took over.

"Lady, this was a custom back in the Civil War. Well-to-do

families in the South buried their money and valuables to keep them out of the hands of those plundering Yankee soldiers. Sometimes they had their trusted slaves do it. Why, I wouldn't be surprised if old Aunt Caroline herself didn't hide the money and jewels here for your father and mother. Then, when they got killed, she was the only one left who knew where they were. And it drove her crazy."

Someone else spoke. "Maybe that's what she's been trying to tell us all these years."

Those motions of fastening something about her neck? It had been necklaces of fabulous value—not a grimy hangman's noose, as everyone had assumed.

Work stopped as they inventoried the treasure. Mrs. Kettering knew that there was more than enough gold here to provide for her adequately for the remainder of her life. In addition, her share of the Lehigh family jewels would make her doubly wealthy. She gave each of the workmen a twenty-dollar gold piece as a bonus and got them to take her and the treasure to the nearest bank, where she deposited the gold in her account and the jewels for safekeeping until they could be disposed of properly.

Aunt Caroline appeared in the vicinity only one more time. This was at her old grave to inspect a handsome new monument Mrs. Kettering had erected in honor of the old slave woman whose loyalty had extended far beyond the grave.

And this time, her old hands didn't bother to fasten anything around her neck, nor did she kick the ground. Before she faded, it looked as if her old hands were raised in hallelujah triumph and her old feet were dancing a jig.

THE GHOST WHO PRACTICED DYING

BART AND SAM, two down-and-out sawmill hands and farm laborers, slept on a homemade bed in a long-vacated, two-story log house in the Montgomery County section of the Uwharries. They slept quite peacefully for several nights, but one night they were awakened by a strange commotion.

Fast and laborious breathing came from under their bed. It sounded as though someone had spent himself in a furious footrace and now lay exhausted and gasping for breath there on the floor under the bed.

"That you breathing so hard?" Bart asked his companion.

"N-naw," Sam quaked, "I—I thought it wuz you."

They got up and lit the candle and looked under the bed. They saw nothing but the bare floor.

"Just the wind a-howling, I guess." Bart shrugged.

By the time they got settled in bed and were dozing again, the ragged breathing commenced once more. This time it turned into pitiful moaning and groaning, punctuated here and there with a painful shriek, as if the victim writhed in dreadful agony. Then came a spasm of gasping and coughing as the victim struggled for breath. Apparently, he did lose his breath then, for a series of choked grunts, snorts, and gasps sounded loudly in the still room, followed by the death rattle in his throat. The latter sound came simultaneously with a staccato beat of shoe heels jerking against the floor. Then silence—oppressive silence.

"S-somebody's done died here in this room," Sam moaned feebly.

"Somebody has died, and we gotta find out who."

They looked under the bed again, more than half expecting to see a human body, but they saw only the bare, grainy, dusty boards of the floor. Bart grabbed the remains of a forgotten straw broom and poked under the bed, just to make sure. But this produced nothing. They looked in the next room, and then all over the house, without finding any sign of anyone or anything dead, or dying, or even in distress.

They bedded down again, and the rest of the night passed uneventfully.

The next day, the two skittish men visited their nearest neighbors, related the events of the night before, and asked if such sounds had been heard there previously.

No one they talked to had ever heard the strange sounds of death, but they told Bart and Sam about other spooky things that had occurred there.

"They's been people kilt and died in that old house before," one old man whispered to them darkly. "One of the meanest men ever lived died there in that room where you've got your bed. That man wuz so mean that one night one of his slaves took a carving knife and stabbed him clean through the heart. The old man was a long time groaning and dying. A few days later they caught the slave, wild and half-insane with fear, and lynched him on one of them big trees by the house. Folks claim that the old man's ghost, or the slave's ghost—or mebbe both—still hang around there. I dunno. I've seen lights and strange goings-on there at night many a time, but I don't rightly know what it is. Most people just leave that place alone."

Sam wanted to vacate the place before dark, but Bart refused. A steady rain began falling late that afternoon, and, anyway, they had no other place to go. After supper they sat around a flickering candle and talked until bedtime. They were just surrendering to welcome sleep when the commotion started.

The performance was much the same as before. It began with

ragged breathing and gradually developed into pitiful moaning, raw gasping, choking, coughing, the death rattle, and the sharp rapping of shoe heels on the floor. It lasted nearly fifteen minutes.

Soon after it started, Bart lit his candle and looked under the bed. He was convinced that the sound originated there, but he could see nothing. Sam sat upright, his teeth chattering, the skimpy covers hugged about him. The candle caused flamboyant shadows to dance around the walls and ceiling like Persian horsemen flashing scimitars.

"Blow it out, blow it out," Sam begged, dropping his face into the covers. "I can't stand them creepy things crawling all over me."

When the light went out, the darkness seemed to amplify the ghastly sounds of the person dying. Sam cringed in the covers. Bart sat stiffly upright and attentive. When the performance ended with the same heel-rapping and exhalation of the last breath, ominous silence pressed down upon them, and sleep came.

Sam made up his mind to leave the next morning, but Bart persuaded him to stay on for another night or two.

"This thing ain't gonna hurt us," Bart reasoned, "else it would've done so already. No use letting it scare us off when we ain't got no place to go anyhow. Mebbe we can figure out what it is. Tonight we'll move the bed into another room and see what happens."

Sam consented reluctantly. That day the partners worked hard all day long at the sawmill deep in the Uwharrie forest two miles from their living quarters. That night they cooked and ate a skimpy supper, then dragged their homemade bedstead into an adjoining room and toppled onto it, too exhausted to undress. Sleep tugging at their eyelids signaled the entrance of the ghost who liked to die.

Virtually the same performance took place again, despite the change in location. The sounds still seemed to come from underneath the bed.

The next night, they pulled the lumpy bedtick off the bedstead and dumped it on the floor where their bed had originally stood.

"Now we'll sleep here on the floor without any space under us and see where the noise comes from," Bart said.

But, just as they were drifting off to sleep, the noise began again. It came plainly and even more realistically from under their makeshift mattress on the floor. This time Bart's temper flared out of control, and he shouted into the darkness for the noise to stop and go away and quit pestering them. But the dying ghost ignored him, and the sounds continued to the end.

Sam deserted the old house the next day, in spite of Bart's insistent pleas that he remain.

"Something mighty evil around this place, Bart," Sam said. "You may git hurt if you stay on here. Thompson said we could sleep in his barn till we can do better. That's where I'm going, and I wish you'd come too. You can't fight a ghost."

But Bart stayed, determined to expose the mysterious forces present in the old house.

Bart stopped coming to work at the sawmill, and Sam grew worried about him. He got off work early one afternoon and went by the old house. He found Bart sitting immobile on an old box with a big stick in his hand. He was staring at the bed against the wall. When Sam made his presence known, Bart looked at him with open hostility flaring in his face and eyes. It required considerable effort for him to recognize his former buddy. The eyes that raked over Sam were too bright, too feverish, too diabolical to be those of a sane man.

"He's cracking, he's cracking up," Bart mumbled. "I'm beating it out of him. He's giving up."

His voice, erratic and shaky, alternated between a whisper and a crescendo of exultation. He muttered and ranted, ignoring Sam altogether.

Sam noticed the bed. It had been beaten and thrashed to bits. Then he saw that the floor boards under the bed, already affected with dry rot, had been shredded by the brutal blows from the stick. There was a subfloor underneath. Hurriedly, he tore up the shat-

The Ghost Who Practiced Dying   57

tered boards. He leaned down to look at the subfloor, and then stepped back in horror. What was it there on the rough pine boards? Stain? Dark, dark stain? Faint drops and one large dark puddle? Didn't the stain have a faded crimson, rusty tinge? Blood? Had the life blood of a mortally wounded man gushed out there on those uneven boards and dripped between the cracks? Sam drew in a hissing breath and turned to Bart. Bart laughed, and it was the fiendish cackle of a madman.

"When he starts to dying, I jump outta bed and start whupping him with my stick, and he starts groaning harder and hollering louder," Bart muttered. "And the harder I beat him, the harder he takes on and the more he suffers. I whup him so hard he shows hisself. The devil shows hisself." Again he laughed the horrible laugh of the crazed. "He can't stand my beatings. He comes out of his hiding place. Ol' Smoky comes out. He's made outta smoke. A smoky ghost. He comes out, and I see pictures."

Sam shivered as Bart whirled to face him.

"You know what I see in them smoky pictures? I see the wicked face of a man. He has a knife, and he kills another man. Then I see this same face, and it's red and purple and full of fear. And there's a hangman's noose around his neck."

Sam wanted to run away, but he wanted to take his sick friend. He gripped Bart by the shoulder.

Bart wheeled around, his eyes blazing and his teeth bared in fury. He brandished the stick menacingly. Sam backed toward the door. As he left, he saw Bart turn back to his lonely vigil at the bed.

That evening, Sam hurried from farm to farm telling the men about Bart and asking them to go with him the next day to subdue the man and get him off to jail or to a hospital.

A warm sun bathed the countryside the next morning when a group of men arrived and circled the house cautiously, expecting to have to use force to capture a savagely crazy person. But they found no one at home. They searched all the rooms, under the

house, around it, and in all the outbuildings. Bart was not to be found.

Sam noticed immediately a change in the atmosphere of the old house. Some of the clammy gloom and creepiness had left it. A bird chirped on the eaves. A stray cat meowed near the door. Sunshine and breezes through the open door swept away the taint of the supernatural. The bed looked much as Sam remembered it from the day before. On the floor, rolled halfway under the bed, lay Bart's stick, the big end severely battered and frayed.

Sam wanted to show the men who had come with him the rusty stains of blood that he had seen the day before. He motioned for them to approach the hole in the floor, but when they looked down at it, they froze in terror. The dark spots on the rough boards of the subfloor were no longer stains. Now they were fresh, warm, red blood, still moving and puddling and running through the cracks and shimmering in the sunlight—as if it had dropped only seconds before from the open wound of a dying man.

Bart was never found, nor was he ever seen or heard of again.

Some folks thought he wandered off into the forest in his delirium and stumbled into the yawning mouth of some forgotten gold-mine shaft in the hills. Some said he got so scared of something in the house that he fled the country under cover of darkness. Others were of the opinion that he drowned himself in the rushing Pee Dee River a few miles away. A few people thought that the ghost Bart had beaten out of the house took him back with it to its lair.

Later occupants of the old house discovered something on the wall which kept alive the story of the ghost who practiced dying. In fact, many visitors came just to see it.

There on the wall over the spot where the bed had once stood, a knot in the solid pine had split. Cracks had appeared around it, and through those cracks rosin had seeped out and dried in unusual designs. Everyone who looked at the configuration on the wall said that it clearly resembled just one thing: a man's face and head—a man with a hangman's noose pulled tightly around his neck.

THE GHOSTS OF THE KRON GOLD

"DAT'S WHAT Lanky Dan, my uncle, told me evah time," Birdsy Ponds declared to the Sikes brothers for the third time in as many days.

"Yeah, we know, but tell it again, slow and careful like, because we got to know it all, with nothing left out," Aaron Sikes drawled. He shifted his tobacco wad, and his teeth popped together like a bear trap clanging shut. His baleful eyes pierced the Negro.

"And you'd better get some conviction into your voice," his brother Asa warned, "because if you're lying to us, nigger, we'll grease up all this ground around here with your stinking carcass."

"Good Lawdy no, I ain't lyin'! I knows better than to lie to you boys, 'cause you is mean an' tough an' fearless, an' you'd stomp me. Naw Suh, it's de gospel truth. Just what Lanky Dan told me many a time befo' he died. He was handyman to de famous ol' doctor, Dr. Francis J. Kron, who doctored people up and down dis river country for fifty years. Fine ol' man. Made lots of money. Dey say his wife had money, too."

"Go on, nigger, get to the point," Aaron threatened.

Birdsy settled down and began his story again.

"One cold fall day back in de late seventies—dis was several years befo' he died—de doctor had Lanky Dan come and git a heavy ol' oaken keg with iron bands around it and roll it down de hill to de inside of one of de three old slave shacks rottin' away dere 'tween de Lowder Ferry Road and de crick. Dere dey left it. Lanky Dan said he couldn't more'n budge one end, let alone lift de whole keg. He said it rattled and clinked lak it was almost full of gold pieces or somethin' mighty clanky. De doctor nevah did say what was in it or what he intended to do with it. 'Just leave it right heah' was all he told Lanky Dan.

"A few days later, he had Lanky Dan come back and hep 'im burn dem three old shacks to de ground. Dey was 'bout rotten down anyway. An' dat's all. Nobody evah seed dat keg of gold again. For years Lanky Dan didn't tell nobody 'bout it. But befo' he died, he figured he'd better tell it, so he told me and my family, since he lived with us. Seemed lak he enjoyed tellin' it, once he got started. He wanted somebody to go look for dat gold and find it. But he said be keerful, 'cause to his dying day he allus believed dat ol' Doctor Kron left a bunch of ghostes behind to guard over dat gold and scare away anybody prowlin' around.

"An' dat's why I's telling you A. Sikeses. Since all de Kron family has died out, and de place is not lived in, I wants you to hep me go find dat gold, an' we'll divide it. I's knowed you A. Sikes Boys a long time, an' I knows you is not afeered of no ghostes. But take me—I's got a strong back, but my gumption is weak."

Aaron Sikes and his brother Asa thought about it a long time and asked Birdsy many questions. They were veterans of many tough encounters and had the reputation of fearing nothing. They were known as the A. Boys, the A. Sikes Boys, or the A. Sikeses. Now they made up their minds: they had to have that Kron gold—ghosts or no ghosts.

Several days later Asa and Aaron drove their mules and wagon to Mt. Gilead to borrow a gold-finding machine from Uncle Juice Whitmire, itinerant inventor and tinkerer, who instructed them in its use and who bargained for a percentage of any loot they found with it. While Aaron practiced with the machine, Asa talked to people who remembered the Krons, trying to establish some factual basis for Birdsy's tale about the keg of gold. From his research he concluded that the story was quite probable. But he also heard references to the ghosts that still hung around the Kron place and to the fearsome things they might do to intruders.

One breezy fall morning the A. Sikeses put their machine in the wagon, went by to pick up Birdsy, and drove out to the Kron place, which was situated in a trough on the northwestern side of what is now Morrow Mountain State Park. They found the location of the old slave shacks in a small cornfield lying on a bit of level bottom-land between the wagon road and a small creek. Thickly wooded ridges and folds of the ancient Uwharrie Mountains surrounded the area, which was dominated by Hattaway Mountain looming impressively to the south. Aaron quickly got the machine into action.

After an hour or two, they got a good reaction from the machine in a spot which Birdsy said could easily be just the place Lanky Dan had described. They tried the machine all over the area, but nowhere did it react so intensely and positively as there amid the cornstalks near the center of the little field at the foot of the mountain. To mark the spot, Asa took an axe and drove a sharpened stovewood stick into the soil.

Elated and bubbling, Birdsy wanted to start digging immediately. The A. Boys said the risk of being spotted from the road was too great, so they would have to return at night to dig.

"Den tonight, tonight!" Birdsy begged. "Let's come tonight and dig and git our hands on some of dat good ol' gold money. Ummm-ummm!"

"No, not tonight," Asa said. "This is Saturday. This is the night of the shindig at the Marks House. Hell, we can't miss that—not all them purty women and that music and the chicken stew and Cousin Moreland's moonshine—can we, Aaron?"

Aaron nodded assent, his eyes already dreamy with visions of the night's anticipated activity.

Birdsy pouted. "I was so wantin' to git my hands on some of dat gold money tonight," he moaned. Then he brightened. "Den, do me dis one favor, Mr. Asa and Mr. Aaron. On de way back, let's us stop by an' ask ol' Aunt Mintie Green about it. It's not far offen de road. She's one of dem witch women. People for miles around comes to her for advice, an' she tells 'em about all de signs and about when de moon is right and all. She conjures up visions and tells 'em all sorts of stuff lak dat. She's good, too, an' I believes in her 'cause she cured my little Lonzo when he's deadly sick last year, an' she told Peaked Howard where his lost beagle was. 'Coase, we'll have to pay her a little bit. But she'll conjure up an' tell us when de time is most favorable to dig for dat gold money and just how to do it 'thout dem ghostes botherin' us. An' she won't talk a word to nobody about it —not if we pays her a little bit. Anyways, she recollects the Kron family, used to work dere some, an' she maybe knows about dis gold—maybe more'n any of us knows."

Aunt Mintie Green lived in a hovel amid the rocks and trees of Feather Bed Hill. Smoke curled from the broken top of a native stone chimney leaning precariously away from the shack, which had rags stuffed in its broken windows. A dog barked as the A. Boys and Birdsy approached. Chickens clucked. Several cats slunk across the big stone door stoop. A nanny goat, heavy with milk, ambled around a corner, baa-ing.

Bonneted and encased in heavy garments, Aunt Mintie didn't look as old or as ugly as most witches, though she did have lines on her face and wisps of white hair straggling from under her bonnet. She knew Birdsy and cackled a greeting, but she eyed the A. Boys suspiciously. Birdsy explained their business and pleaded, almost on bended knees, for her co-operation, handing her two ragged dollar bills. She turned and motioned them inside.

They gathered around a rickety table, from which a lamp flickered, pushing back the murkiness. Aunt Mintie sat down, and Birdsy sat opposite her, watching raptly. The A. Boys stood near, scoffing and smirking. The men watched the woman gradually goad herself into a trance by a series of intense motions of her hands, head, and body, accompanied by singsongy chants, which lapsed into mutters and mumbles. Finally she fell over rigidly to the floor, where for some moments her body jerked and quivered. She shrieked a time or two and foamed at the mouth, and the whites of her eyes flashed wildly. Laboriously, she came back to her senses and reclaimed her place at the table. Birdsy's taut face was one big question.

"I seed it; I seed it all, and hit was purty awful," Aunt Mintie said, breathing heavily. "He buried dat keg of gold just about where you'uns got it marked. But he called down all de ghosts and witches and ha'nts and boogers and all de devil's helpers from de meanest places in de whole world to guard dat gold agin all seekers. Dat's why nobody has found it. De ghosts has drove 'em away. Others has been lookin' for it, but de ghosts allus drive 'em into fits to git away. Dere's only one way to do it."

She lowered her head to the table in concentration. Birdsy rose hastily, his mouth open with a question, but she raised a hand to silence him. After a minute or two of tapping and rubbing her temple, she straightened and continued.

"Hit'll have to be on de exact same day de gold was buried. 'Tween dark and midnight. And only when de moon is full and round. Approach de site from de west. Spit on de ground when you is ten steps away. Walk around de spot three times, den walk backards around it once. Den cross yourself over your heart and look toward de Kron house and say: 'Ye ghosts of de Kron gold, don't you bother me dis night.' An' dat ort to give you protection. But just on dis one anniversary night. To be extra special safe, take a pinch of dis mixture with you. It wards off de evils and de spirits."

She scooped a handful of trashy crumbs from a wooden box and gave each man a pinch of the concoction. Birdsy reverently tucked his into the big pocket of his overalls. The A. Boys promptly discarded theirs, dusted their palms, and stamped their feet in disgust.

"But de day, Aunt Mintie, de day? When is dat best day, or night, to go dig for de gold with no ghostes around?" Birdsy pleaded.

She concentrated again. "It was in de fall, after harvest, on de twenty-first of de month when de moon was exactly full. When

The Ghosts of the Kron Gold

does dat come again? Let me see. . . . Hey, dis is de twenty-first day, today! De moon? De moon is fullin' now. Last night . . . hey, de moon is full tonight! You sho' is lucky. It's tonight! De only favorable time. It may not come again lak dis in years."

On the way back home, Birdsy began to babble about how lucky they were to have consulted Aunt Mintie Green. The A. Boys, however, vehemently cursed her and the results of her conjuring. Not for all the gold in the Uwharrie Mountains would they miss the big shindig at the Marks House tonight, they told Birdsy, ignoring his protests. Sunday night was good enough for them. They told Birdsy to be ready late the next afternoon.

After staying up merrymaking most of the night and sleeping most of the day, the A. Boys were surly and sullen late Sunday afternoon as they hitched the team of mules to the wagon and piled digging tools and a lantern aboard.

Aaron shifted his tobacco and spoke. "You know, Asa, I've been thinking. When we git out there tonight and dig that hole and find that gold . . . what's the use of dividing it three ways? Hadn't you rather have a half than a third? We'll have us a good, deep hole where that keg comes out. Why don't we chuck that lunkhead Birdsy down in the bottom and use his body to help fill it back up? We can get him down deep, cover him good, and scatter dead grass over the top. Then, when that farmer plows up the field again, it will destroy all signs. No one will ever know."

"Makes good sense to me," Asa yawned. "Good sense."

They stopped and picked up Birdsy. He looked jaded, tired, and sleepy.

"What're you lookin' so tired for?" Asa asked the Negro. "We're the ones who stayed up all night."

"I couldn't hardly sleep any all night, just for thinkin' about dat gold," Birdsy told them, a broad grin on his face.

They arrived at the cornfield just after dark, concealed the mules and wagon in the trees off to one side, and lugged the tools to the spot. Asa knelt with the lantern and fumbled in the dirt until he found the stake. He motioned to Birdsy to bring the pick and mattock.

"We ought to make it about two and a half feet square. You dig, and me and Aaron'll shovel."

The moon, a fully round piece of gold, rose over the trees as Birdsy chunked the pick into the earth again and again. An owl hooted in the woods. From far away came the sound of a coon dog on the trail. The lantern, shielded on the side toward the road, cast weird shadows across the whitish cornstalks.

Suddenly they heard a strange noise start from the top of Hattaway Mountain and descend toward them, furiously increasing in speed and volume. It sounded like a huge herd of animals—cattle or buffalo or something even larger—stampeding straight down the mountainside, about to riddle them under thousands of sharp hooves.

"Quick, get back to the wagon!" Asa shouted. They all ran from the little field and into the trees and dived under the wagon just as the thunder of the stampede swept past them. Then all was quiet again.

Birdsy trembled violently as they stood up and edged back out to the hole. "It's de ghostes after us! It's de Kron ghostes. I knows it is. I cain't stand it. I gotta leave. I's a-goin'."

Aaron collared him, propelled him to the hole, then thrust the pick into his unwilling hands. "Dig, black man, dig. No ghosts are gonna run us off after we're this close to that gold. You dig and leave the ghosts to us."

Between licks, Birdsy shuddered. He had finished his digging stint and was catching his breath while the A. Boys shoveled, when a second ghostly noise came from Hattaway Mountain.

This time it sounded like runaway wagons—hundreds of huge, heavy wagons plunging ever faster down the mountain—smashing and battering their way through all obstacles. The noise swelled in a crescendo as it neared them. Moaning, Birdsy fled for the shelter

The Ghosts of the Kron Gold   67

of the trees, and the A. Boys followed. They huddled under their own wagon until the terrible noise went past and faded. Then they crept back out to the hole.

The Negro was having fits to leave that haunted place and go home. But he was afraid to depart alone. And he had no luck persuading the A. Boys to go, though their resolve had weakened some.

"Nothing's hurt us yet," Asa reasoned. "Who minds a little noise? Let's get that gold outta here before they have time to come back again."

But Birdsy was too shaken to control himself. Asa got into the hole and swung the pick. Then Aaron shoveled. Well into his second stint with the pick, Asa heard a popping noise and looked behind him. There sat Birdsy on the dirt pile, his teeth chattering, his body jerking, his eyes huge. All he could do was whimper and moan as his arm pointed upward. When the A. Boys looked up and saw it, they gasped and leaped backward.

A noiseless parade was trooping down the mountain. It was a parade of ghouls and cadavers. Much bigger than life, each figure glowed like the moon as it ambled and rocked and glided down toward the petrified men at the hole. There were dozens of them, and more joined, dropping out of the sky and popping up from the ground. Each had that soulless look about him—the emaciated face, devoid of expression, and the pupilless eyes. Some carried scythes and cudgels. There was a morbid rhythm to their march down the hill. The resoluteness of their march made their coming even more terrifying.

The three men were too astounded and stupified to run. Birdsy sprawled on the dirt pile, while the A. Boys stood on either side of the hole.

As the ghouls drew near, Birdsy squeaked, "Oh Lordy, oh Lordy, do save us, do save us!" He was trying to remember and repeat what Mintie Green had told them, which began: "Ye ghosts of de Kron gold . . . ," but under the tension of the moment, he couldn't recall the rest. So he jabbered that phrase over and over.

When the first scythe-carrying ghoul reached him, Aaron grabbed his shovel and began striking violently at the figure. But his shovel didn't hit anything, and Aaron felt himself flung backward to the ground.

Asa chose to go down fighting, too. He dived at one of the towering figures, seeking to wrestle it to the ground. Instead, he met only thin air and bruised himself in a tumble amid the cornstalks.

One by one, the glowing figures advanced to the edge of the new excavation, threw up their arms and raised their heads in a gesture of supplication, then stepped into the hole and vanished. Soon the entire procession, scythes, cudgels, and all, had been swallowed by the hole.

Minutes passed before the men stirred from their stupor.

"We're dreaming, that's what it is, we're all dreaming," Aaron declared. "And this is a dadburn nightmare!"

"Naw, we ain't so dreaming, either," Asa rejoined, rubbing his skinned knees and scratched face. "What we saw was real. It was there. We all saw it. It was there just like we saw it. There's no denying that."

"De ghostes is warnin' us to leave and don't come back," Birdsy shrilled. "An' please, puh-lease, Mr. A. Boys, let's go now while we is able. It's too late after we gits hurt or kilt. Dey's warnin' us away, and dey cain't make it any mo' plainer. Please let's go, befo' somethin' mo' dreadful happens."

Asa spat on his hands and rubbed them. "What's plain to me is that there is gold in this hole right here. Else them ghosts wouldn't be pranking around here trying to scare us. And we aim to have it. We're almost waist deep now. It can't be much deeper. Let's hurry. Unlimber yourself, nigger, and get that pick a-swinging."

Under the ire of the white man, Birdsy took the pick. Holding the lantern high, he looked carefully in and around the hole, but he could see no sign of the procession of ghouls that had vanished therein. Gingerly he descended into the hole and began digging.

The next time Birdsy's pick struck the soil, the earth trembled so violently that it knocked the men off their feet. Then it stopped. Each time the tool jabbed into the soil, the wounded earth shuddered frighteningly.

Asa swore and cursed and made the Negro get out of the hole so he could try it. For a few licks, the pick worked normally; then, on the next stroke, it refused to come out of the soil where it was buried to the handle. Asa tugged and jerked and kicked and swore, but the pick wouldn't budge. He called for the shovel and thrust it deep into the soil with his heavy boot. It, too, froze there and wouldn't budge under any pressure. He tried the second shovel, and the same thing happened. That left the mattock. With a mighty swing he sunk its wide blade up to the hilt. And there it froze. The black earth imprisoned the tools and refused to let go.

Aaron cursed his brother for being such a clumsy weakling and bade him get out of the hole and let a man take over. On his first try, Aaron succeeded in freeing each of the tools. Then he started to resume digging. But each time the point of the pick or mattock touched the soil, it glanced off with a ring as if the tool had encountered hard granite. The floor of the hole seemed to have solidified against all penetration.

Aaron leaned against the wall of the hole, tore off a fresh chew of tobacco, and looked at the far-off lightning flashes of a rainstorm approaching from the west.

"If this blasted hole keeps on acting queer like this, we won't ever get nothing done," he said. "Damn it all, I'm gonna give it a lick that'll bust something loose somewhere for sure. Git back outta my way."

But Asa and Birdsy hovered up close to watch as Aaron hefted the pick for a Herculean lick that sent the curved spike of metal far into the earth. There came a distinct "klunk" as it apparently struck and penetrated something.

The Ghosts of the Kron Gold   71

From the new pick hole wafted up a strong odor, sweet, oily, sickening—and evil. As soon as it reached the nostrils of the men, they slumped into unconsciousness, Aaron falling against the side of the hole and Asa at its edge. Birdsy fell backward away from the hole and into the cornstalks.

Soon the rainstorm hit. Thunder crashed and rumbled. Lightning jigsawed across the heavens. And it rained and rained and rained.

The A. Boys woke at dawn and found themselves under foul-smelling quilts on the dirt floor of Mintie Green's hovel. Outside, the sun was rising to dry things out. Inside, rain puddles dampened everything. A rooster flapped at the window. The nanny goat baa-ed from near the fireplace, where the witch woman was cooking victuals. Sore and creaky, the A. Boys dragged their bodies up on a bench at the rickety table. Birdsy sat there alert and composed. He waited until they got settled before he spoke.

"I woke up at de hole. It was rainin' cats and dogs. An' I run. I did. I run away. I was so skeered, I just couldn't stop gittin' away from dat place. But den, even in all dat rain, I realized somethin'. You boys was back dere. I said to myself dat maybe you was hurt an' maybe you was daid or needed hep, an' I couldn't run away no mo' an' leave you. So I came back through de rain and lugged you senseless boys outta dat hole dat was already fillin' up with water. I loaded you onto de wagon and trotted de mules heah to de first shelter I knows. An' Aunt Mintie took us in for de night. De mules is fed and rested and ready to go when you are."

Remembering the fantastic occurrences of the night, the A. Boys wanted to go back to the Kron place to see it by daylight. They sat strangely subdued and morose, while Birdsy drove. At the Kron place they stayed on the wagon seat because they could see enough from there, or so they said. Torrents of rain had inundated the little bottom field and completely covered it with silt. The storm had erased their hole and all signs of their presence there. The A. Boys tried to recapture the weird experiences of the previous night, but they couldn't. They rode back home silently, knowing they were men bested by ghosts.

The A. Boys lost their wildness after that, stopped their deviltry, and settled down to become substantial citizens who were a credit to their community. Only rarely did they discuss the Kron gold-seeking episode, but when they did relate that eerie tale, they did so with conviction and with a realism that left hearers gaping. There were few skeptics.

Birdsy and his family left the community pretty quickly after the memorable night at the Kron place. They must have taken Mintie Green with them, too, for she vacated the hovel and was never seen there again. Much later, word drifted back through the grapevine that Birdsy had purchased an interest in a going business up North and that he appeared to be doing right well for himself.

A local legend persists that the Kron gold is still there—part of it, at least. At any rate, the Kron ghosts are still on duty, militant as ever toward intruders who come at the wrong time, which is practically all the time. The only right time to look for the gold and avoid the wrath of the guardian ghosts is between dark and midnight when the moon is exactly full on the exact anniversary of the day the gold was buried. Or else find yourself a new conjure woman.

PRIVATE CORRIHER'S GHOST

DURING ARMY MANEUVERS in the early years of World War II, a small group of trainees and one officer were sent on a special scouting and tactical mission deep into the Uwharries. Led by a jeep, the big "Six by Six" truck pulled a long-barreled piece of heavy artillery. The detail came to a stop late one afternoon in a remote glen, and the men set about making camp while the truck backed the big gun into a prominent position.

A new soldier, wearing a strange gray uniform, suddenly appeared in their midst and addressed their officer in a voice quivering with excitement and urgency.

"Cap'n, our scouts bring word that a big enemy band is just over the hill and is coming to attack us. The hosses is all unhitched and tired out. But we gotta protect that gold in the cannon. What can we do?"

Surprisingly, their officer responded to him.

"Quick, Private Corriher, let's hide the cannon. Let's push it over the bank into this small lake so the water will hide it from them. We'll come back for it later. All right, men, move!"

The men looked around for a few bewildered seconds. They were wearing uniforms of Confederate gray like Private Corriher. Their jeep and truck had changed into horses and mules and wagons. Their big howitzer was now a bulky wheeled cannon, with its muzzle tightly plugged. It was sitting on the brink of a tiny lake. Coming toward them from beyond the trees were the faint sounds of a bugle and of a body of horsemen in motion.

Several of the men rushed to assist the captain and Private Corriher. They hoisted the big gun's muzzle, exceedingly heavy, and shoved the cannon backward down the steep bank toward the water. Private Corriher felt a tug on his trouser leg and discovered, too late, that his clothing had become caught on the chassis of the cannon carriage. As the unstoppable cannon gained momentum, he realized the doom awaiting him, and a piercing cry of terror burst from his lips, ending in a watery gurgle as the waters closed over man and gun.

Unable to save the man, the other soldiers turned toward their horses and weapons to try to fight or flee. But the attacking Union cavalry was upon them in overwhelming numbers. Rifles cracked and spat. Swords flashed and fell. Mortally wounded men fell groaning across the already dead. Horses snorted. The bugler stopped. Now all the men in gray lay dead around the campsite.

The members of the World War II Army detail began picking themselves up off the ground where they had fallen. Wide-eyed and bewildered, they looked at themselves and their equipment, normal again, and touched each other to see if they were real. They began bubbling questions.

"Fantastic!" the officer blurted. "I don't believe it—but it happened. Somehow we blundered back into a Civil War battle here. That's what it must have been. We were all wearing Confederate gray. The attackers were Union cavalry troops. But they killed us all! There were no survivors." The officer paused a minute, thinking. "There was no one left to come back for that cannon with the Confederate gold in it. It may still be around here somewhere. Maybe that's why Private Corriher appeared to us—to let us know—so we could find the gold and finally set him free!"

The Army detail was so shaken by the experience of fighting again an eighty-year-old battle and being annihilated by the enemy that it abandoned its mission and went back to maneuver headquarters to report the phenomenon. The officers in charge dismissed the story as imagination and fantasy; they did not dignify it by so much as a written report. They reprimanded the officer severely for abandoning his assignment and shipped him and all his men out to the fighting zones with the next contingent.

World War II ended. The officer, Waldo Severs, came back to the Uwharries to check into the experience he and his men had had there a few years previously. He walked with a limp now, and his body carried scars from genuine wounds. In his respites from the war, Severs had studied Civil War history and learned that it was not at all improbable that the Army of the Confederate States of America had cached part of its gold in the maw of a cannon, which circulated among the battle zones to meet payrolls and pay for stores. He found it quite conceivable that such a highly-secret cannon detail had been hiding amid the deeply forested Uwharrie hills to await its next clandestine rendezvous when a marauding Union cavalry detachment stumbled upon it and wiped it out to a man. He thought it equally likely that the victors, in their subsequent reconnaissance of the area, had failed to discover the gold-laden cannon submerged in the tiny lake, along with its guardian corpse. Would not both still be there awaiting liberation?

Severs spent weeks rambling in the hills, trying to find the spot. It proved impossible. Other groups on maneuver had bulldozed new trails through the forests. Logging operations had changed the appearance of the land. New undergrowth added to the confusion. Hundreds of spots could have been the right one. Realizing that he would not recognize the place even if he did stumble on it, Severs began systematically interviewing the residents of the area.

He talked to people who knew fragments of the story but found no one who could give a cohesive account. Then one bearded oldster recounted a tale that injected a new dimension into the story and fanned fresh interest.

"That flaring light is connected with it some way," the oldster told Severs. "The blazing light starts down low, shoots out of the ground like a burning brush pile, and leaves a trail of light and sparks till it all vanishes in the sky. Can't rightly tell where it comes from. Some'rs here in these hills. It just suddenly lights up and kinda roars and whistles for a few seconds, and it's gone. I only seen it once myself. But others who was in the war have seen it, too. My father saw it a coupla times. He believed it was the ghost of a Civil War soldier firing off a flare or cannon so someone would come and find him and set him free."

Other natives who had seen the flaring light and heard about it shared this belief, but none could pinpoint the location.

One day it dawned on Severs that perhaps only military movements incited action by the ghost of Private Corriher. He bought a surplus Army jeep, dressed in full military garb, and began prowling the forest trails in the early nighttime hours. Soon he was rewarded. One evening a shaft of light arced over the trees in a dazzling streak. He saw it quite well, but he could not determine its origin. Nor could he locate it in subsequent sightings.

Then another idea occurred to Severs. Maybe the ghost demanded something more realistic before it would respond. After doing some research into Civil War military uniforms, Severs obtained the authentic uniform of a captain in the Army of the Confederate States of America, complete with insignia, epaulettes, sword, and boots, as well as fancy saddle and bridle trappings for his horse. Fully dressed now in the authentic Southern captain's uniform, Severs rode his old horse over the trails. Not only did he see the ghost cannon firing off again, but one day the gray-clad ghost of Private Corriher appeared to him on a forest trail. Severs scrambled off his horse and approached the figure.

"Private Corriher, this is your captain. I've come back for you and the cannon and the gold. Show me where to look."

Ever the alert guard, the ghost of Private Corriher jerked its long gun to the ready and stepped forward.

"The password?" it demanded. "What's the password?"

Severs did not know the password. He tried to guess. "Down with the Union!" "Victory over Grant!" "The Confederacy forever!"

None of these passwords or others Severs gave satisfied the ghost, and it soon vanished.

Severs became obsessed with the idea of finding the gold. He grew oblivious of everything around him. Afflicted with a progressively worsening dementia, he rode his decrepit horse over the forest trails day and night. The mousy gray uniform, which he did not bother to wash, grew sour and moldy. Corrosion dulled the sword and scabbard which flapped at his side. As he rode through the countryside, he spouted words in unending combinations in a pathetic effort to hit upon the password, attract the ghost of Private Corriher, and unlock its secret.

Severs might still be riding his old horse and mumbling odd phrases on his demented mission through the Uwharrie forests, had not a slightly tipsy hunter mistaken him for a deer and shot and killed him late one winter day. Unclaimed and unidentified, he was buried by the county in a cemetery nearby. It appeared that, with his death, the mission of Private Corriher's ghost would be forever unfulfilled.

Then, in the mid-1960's, the U.S. Army's John F. Kennedy Center for Special Warfare at Fort Bragg, North Carolina, made extensive use of the Uwharries as a training ground for operations in psychological, guerrilla, and unconventional warfare. Late one afternoon a small group of Special Forces men led by one officer jeeped far into the Uwharrie forests on a special assignment. As they were making preparations for camp, they were surprised by a young soldier, dressed in a strange gray uniform, who appeared out of the trees and rushed up to their officer with an urgent message:

"Cap'n, our scouts bring word that a big enemy band is just over the hill and is coming to attack us. The hosses is all unhitched and tired out. But we gotta protect that gold in the cannon. What can we do?"

THE GHOSTS IN THE BURNING LOGS

Neighbors first learned of Rose Bullock's death about church time one April Sunday morning. A little girl, maybe eight or nine, walked listlessly up to the Tom Duffy home just as the family was preparing to leave for church.

"My daddy says for you to come down there," she said. Her words sounded rehearsed. "My mommy is dead. He wants you to come on down there now."

Big-eyed and solemn, she turned and walked back down the path.

Tom and Mabel Duffy looked at each other horrified. "Let's go," Tom said. They followed the child.

Church services were forgotten, and a crowd soon gathered at the dilapidated Bullock home in a bottom down near the creek. Most of the neighbors stood around outside, while a few at a time went inside to view the remains of the dead woman on a bed in the back room.

Most of the woman's clothes had been burned off, and her flesh was seared and charred. Her arms and face were smudged and blackened with grime. Ashes and soot soiled her long hair.

Mabel Duffy spoke up. "We saw her working all day long yesterday, cutting and piling up brush and trees in the new ground. I talked with her at the spring around dinnertime. Said she was working hard to please her husband so he'd let her go visit her maw today. But she had to make herself a new dress first. I saw a lamp burning down here long past bedtime last night, and I knew she must be working on that new dress."

Rance Bullock, Rose's husband and the father of the several unkempt children lolling around the yard, answered questions guardedly. His eyes were bloodshot, his hair disheveled. The scent of homebrew fouled his breath.

"She got up way late in the night to go out yonder and see about the log fire in the new ground," he said, motioning toward a still-smoking pile of small trees and brush in a partially-cleared field a few hundred yards away. I went back to sleep. When I woke up, she wasn't here. I went out looking for her and found her there in the edge of the fire. I carried her back to the bed, but she died."

The women began laying out the body of Rose Bullock in preparation for burial, deciding to bury her in the new dress that she had completed. Other women consoled the children and took them to their homes for clothing and food. A messenger was dispatched to tell the dead woman's parents.

Bullock sauntered out to a bench between two trees, where he sat down and whittled. His hands jerked, and one could sense a scared-rabbit nervousness behind the griefless calm on his face. Occasionally a man came by to put a hand on his shoulder and express sympathy. The preacher from the church, where services had been suspended, came to talk with Bullock. But Bullock's only response was a request that they hurry up and get the burying over with so that he and his poor little children would be through with it all.

Some of the boys and younger men wandered down to the new ground to check Rose Bullock's log fire. Smoke rose steadily from the pile, and intermittently there licked out a ragged line of flame, which flickered brightly until again subdued by the heavy smoke. There was something peculiar about that fire.

Abruptly the men in the yard were startled by a shout from the group at the burning pile. The boys waved and motioned frantically. All save Bullock trotted to the fire.

As they watched, two clouds of smoke rose out of the pile and seemed to assume human shapes, one a powerfully-built man, the other a delicate woman with long hair. The strong male figure of smoke wobbled drunkenly. Its arms went out to grab the neck of the female figure. As the two smoke-figures struggled for a moment or two, observers could see the stronger one violently strike, shake, and choke the weaker one. The limp female figure then crumpled.

Few would have thought much of the spectacle had it ended there. But the smoke-figures repeated their performance a second time, then a third.

An older man called to a grown boy. "Go in the house and tell the women what we've seen. Tell them to examine the dead woman's throat for fingermarks and her head for bruises. Then come back and let us know."

After a while, the boy returned to the men still watching the fire. Yes, whitish fingermarks plainly showed around her swollen throat after they had washed off the grime. And bruises suggesting a beating were found on her face and head.

One man rasped to the others, "That's what this fire's been showing us! That sorry drunken bum choked his wife to death with his own hands. Then, to cover up, he took her body out to this fire and burned it to make it look like the fire killed her!"

Everyone thought so. Even the law. But the old sheriff could prove nothing. When Bullock was confronted with the suspicions, he grew sullen and indignant, stubbornly insisting that his wife had accidentally fallen into the fire and burned to death. Officially, that's the way the matter ended.

But log fires in Uwharrie new-ground fields kept the matter alive. A great deal of curiosity and ceremony sprang up in connection with new-ground fires, particularly those that were ornery about burning or that belched out smoke and jagged arms of flame. Around many such fires, people gathered to watch as two figures of smoke emerged and repeated the same performance they had given that day in the creek bottom while Rose Bullock lay dead in her home.

Through the years the people who witnessed and worked around such fires, knowing the story of Rose Bullock, would bare their heads and stand reverently while watching the figures of smoke. They called it a sign—a symbol of grave injustice. Some of them uttered dark comments as to what ought to be done with that murderous husband who had killed his wife with apparent impunity.

Bullock continued his dissolute life and proved too sorry to provide and care adequately for his children, who were placed with relatives and other people in the community for a decent upbringing. Bullock wandered off and stayed away for twenty years or longer. Then he came back to settle down again at his old home in the creek bottom, which had been virtually swallowed by the encroaching forest. He lived there alone and made a little money by setting fish traps in the creek and making moonshine back in the wilds along the stream. More years passed. Few people ever saw Bullock any more, the forest concealed his abode and his activities so well.

Changes were taking place in the Uwharries. No longer did the big farmers clear their new farmland laboriously by hand. Now bulldozers tore and gouged ruthless swaths as they pushed trees, stumps, and debris back out of the fields and into the draws and ravines to be leveled over, ready for the plow. Big piles of logs were seldom burned any more.

Eventually a big farm operator bought a large tract along the creek that included the Bullock land, on which taxes had been delinquent for years. Immediate clearing operations were begun. Machines growled, and the forest receded before them. One day the workmen found themselves facing an ancient clapboard shack before which sat a white-headed old man whittling on a stick. They spared the shack temporarily. Because of the terrain, they decided to burn the forest rubble. Not far from the shack, they bulldozed up a huge tangle of logs and forest growth and set fire to it.

Before they knocked off for the day, the workmen, proffering a bottle of whiskey, engaged the old man at the shack to watch the big fire for them and to keep it from spreading into a patch of broom sedge nearby.

Early the next morning Tom Duffy, now an old man, came out on his hillside porch. The big fire had burned down some. Suddenly he saw what appeared to be the body of a man. Hurriedly he got his cane and hobbled down the rough spring path to the scene.

Near the edge of the fire lay the body of Rance Bullock. Most of his clothes had been burned off and still smouldered in places. He had been burned badly, especially around his head. One sightless eye was still recognizable. It was stretched wide in terror.

Then Tom Duffy saw something that caused him to shout for his wife to come down and look.

There were deep, evenly-spaced streaks of badly-burned flesh all around Bullock's scrawny throat. The realization staggered him. The burns looked just as if two hands had clutched Bullock's throat and choked him to death with fingers of flame.

MILLIE CROCKET

MILLIE CROCKET was already an old woman and a drinking woman the first time most people remember seeing her. She and her big brood of kids of obscure lineage occupied a tumbledown shack in the edge of the pine field, where the wind sighed in the pinetops and the sunlight in the early morn filtered down in misty beams. Dozens of bare feet kept the yard packed and clean and hungry-looking. By the time her children had married off, left the shack, and relegated her to a life of loneliness there, Millie had a craving for alcohol which the people of the community came to know quite well.

They say that every time a can of beer was punctured, whether out in the open or inside a dwelling, Millie, if she wasn't already too far under the influence, would cock her head as if she had already heard the familiar "paw-shoosh" of the escaping air, catch the tangy scent of the alcohol in her nostrils, then slowly turn around with her nose elevated like a radar scanning antenna. When she made a contact and pointed the location, she headed that way. Nothing stopped her. Later, you could see her shuffling back along the road or path, happily guzzling a bottle or can of beer.

When the alcoholic spirits that Millie zeroed in on were inside a dwelling and the door was locked, Millie would pound the door with her fists and bawl for someone to come out and hand her a drink. If the door wasn't locked, she would walk right in with never an apology or a thought that her abrupt appearance might be inopportune. It got so that a man and woman doing a little love-making on the sly in some abandoned shanty weren't safe any more, especially if they did a little drinking with their wooing, as most of them did. Some of these lovers, always half-expecting Millie to show up at just the wrong time, would even take the precaution of setting an open can of beer conspicuously outside the door or window, then barricade themselves inside with a feeling of security.

Lovers in parked cars would leave Millie's portion of their booze somewhere close by so that she might come and get her drink and leave without disturbing them.

Moonshiners in the hills were practically scared out of their skins when the old colored woman would break out of the brush and stride purposefully up to the still for a drink. Some even threatened to shoot until they learned that she would keep their clandestine operations safe in exchange for a jug of beer or brew.

Although a still got busted up from time to time by the reve-nooers, no one ever accused Millie of squealing on the moonshiners. As, indeed, she did not. Folks said the old woman acted with a shrewd intelligence when it came to self-interest.

Occasionally hoboes and other riffraff, too lazy to shift for their own whiskey, tried to follow Millie on her alcoholic safaris and horn in on some of the liquid loot. This made Millie stomping mad. She sensed their motives and jealously glowered them into turning back. She shared her hard-won drinks with no one.

In the last years of her life, Millie had a little money of her own to spend for drink. Her monthly welfare check from the county was supplemented occasionally by shady male characters who left a few coins after visiting her crumbling shack. With this pittance of cash income, Millie was able to buy a portion of her alcoholic needs. So she began to slow down on radaring for drinks. Anyway, she was becoming too decrepit now to go waddling all over the neighborhood following the alcoholic scents in the air waves, especially at night and over rough terrain to the moonshine stills.

Millie's favorite place to buy whiskey and beer—in fact, the only convenient place in the Negro community—was at Beulah Bolen's house. Almost everyone knew that Beulah sold the stuff. The law knew it, too, but never bothered her unless the complaints got too heavy. They figured it was better to let the Negroes buy their liquor in their own neighborhood than to have them weave drunkenly over the county roads and maybe kill someone or get killed.

Beulah did a pretty thriving business. But she was mighty peculiar about her customers. You didn't just go in and say, "Gimme a beer." First you looked around to make sure that there were no strange faces among the loungers in the room. Then you rapped on the cabinet top at the rear of Beulah's main room. Two raps for a beer. Three for a drink of whiskey. After Beulah saw the color of your money, she disappeared through the curtained partition, and you could hear the refrigerator door open and close. Then, if the coast was still clear, you got your drink. But Beulah maintained strict discipline about no one ever asking for a drink. She made you rap for it.

One late October night, after patronizing Beulah's place, Millie did not make it all the way back to her shack in the pines. The next morning they found her sprawled on her face in the broom sedge at the edge of the road, her body stiff, her sightless eyes stretched wide, her mouth and face soiled with half-frozen dirt. Death had frozen one of her outflung hands around a beer can which still contained a little liquid.

They buried old Millie in a lonely grave under the pines. The wind provided a mournful elegy.

Several years passed. Beulah's place was raided a few times by the law, and the colored woman was given a stern warning and placed on probation by the county judge.

Then a new preacher took over at Shiloh AME Zion Church. Beulah took a cottoning to him, and she got religion and professed before everyone at the Big Meeting that she was a changed woman. The new preacher baptized her with the other converts in the Badin Lake backwater.

And straightway she smashed all her whiskey bottles and poured out all her beer and got rid of the containers, telling all her customers that she was out of business for good. No amount of anguished pleading could make her reconsider.

Beulah took up sewing and gardening, cultivating beautiful flowers in her yard. She taught the young people at the church. She and the preacher were on the verge of getting married when something happened to upset their plans.

One late summer night, Beulah had settled her creaky bones in bed, and sleep had almost claimed her, when a commotion startled her awake. Someone must be knocking at her door, she thought. She snapped on her electric lights and peered outside. No one was there. No response came to her hail. She switched off the lights and went back to bed. But no sooner had she gotten settled than the noise came again. This time she heard it more clearly.

Rap-rap-rap.

She sat upright in bed, shivers of fear crawling over her taut body.

Rap-rap-rap.

She recognized the noise now. It sounded exactly like one of her former customers rapping on the cabinet top for a drink of whiskey.

But who? Why? Everyone knew that she had stopped selling it long ago.

She had fastened all the doors and windows securely. No one could have gotten into the house without awakening her.

As she sat there thinking, the rap-rap-rap sounded again, louder and more insistent this time, as if the customer were mighty impatient.

She switched on her lights once more and looked into the main room at the cabinet, but she saw nothing amiss. Beulah kept the lights burning and sat huddled by the fireplace. The rapping continued at broken intervals until midnight, when it suddenly stopped and was heard no more. Midnight, Beulah remembered with a shudder, was when she had closed up her former business and shooed everyone out of her house.

The next morning her neighbors and friends listened skeptically

Millie Crocket   87

to her description of the nocturnal rapping on her cabinet top. But she persuaded a few of her friends, including the new preacher, to sit up with her that night and listen for the noise. They heard it plainly. All were mystified as the rapping continued, sometimes insistently, at odd intervals until midnight.

It was too much for Beulah. She burst out in a hysterical scream: "It's Millie Crocket! That's who it is. It sounds just like old Millie coming to get her drink."

Someone suggested that Beulah take a can of beer and set it out on the cabinet top the next night to see if it would stop the ghostly rapping. Reluctantly, Beulah accepted the beer and kept it chilled in her refrigerator until that evening around bedtime, when she and a larger group of her friends, many of them former customers, sat up waiting. When the rapping sounded, as they somehow knew it would, Beulah got up and vanished through the curtained partition. The refrigerator door opened and closed. Beulah came back and set an opened can of beer on the cabinet top.

Witnesses gave different accounts of what happened next. Most agreed that the can of beer rose and arched up with the contents gurgling out exactly as if into the invisible mouth and down the invisible throat of an invisible person. But no liquid spilled on the floor. Of that everyone was sure.

At any rate, pandemonium broke loose. Howling, screaming Negroes poured out the windows and doors. The whole community became alarmed as the witnesses rushed from house to house to tell about the ghost at Beulah's place.

Beulah entered the house but once more: that was the next day to supervise the moving out of all her belongings to a friend's home half a mile away. She grew withdrawn, and her romance with the new preacher cooled.

In subsequent months after the incident at Beulah's place, it became apparent that Millie's ghost—it couldn't be anything else, the villagers said—was back on the prowl, again industriously radaring

for drinks. They knew, because the ghost was encountered at many of Millie's former haunts and its actions closely followed the pattern of Millie's behavior a few years previously.

No opened or accessible bottle of alcoholic beverage was safe any longer. More than once someone reported that he had started to lift a frosty can of beer toward his mouth and felt it wrenched from his fingers before it reached his lips.

Secreted lovers again were frightened by banging on the door, by seeing some of their whiskey or beer rise and vanish before their eyes, by knowing they might never really be alone.

One Saturday night two couples who had been parked in a car off the road clamored into the village, hysterically shouting that several opened cans of beer they had had sitting in the car had mysteriously floated out the open windows.

Occasionally a moonshiner came in, wild-eyed and raving, telling a fantastic tale about a jug of freshly-distilled booze that went floating, quite by itself, down through the bushes, gently jogging to and fro, and that at times arched upward, tilted, and paused perfectly still for long seconds as the liquid gurgled out with never a drop spilling on the ground.

Even some special homemade blackberry wine that the preacher had obtained for use in commemorating the Lord's Supper at the church on Sunday morning vanished before it reached its destination.

Beer-guzzling and whiskey-drinking still go on at fish fries, community picnics, dances, and private parties around the area. Perhaps more now than ever before. Many of them start with a brief and simple placatory gesture, often unnoticed, its significance lost on the younger people in the group. A man will puncture a cold can of beer and set it down gently on a stump or rock or on the end of the picnic table, with the mumbled remark, half to himself:

"This one's for old Millie."

THE FIDDLER'S GHOST DANCERS

WHEN MARCUS O'MALLEY got a few slugs of corn liquor in his belly, he could make a fiddle wail and talk to you with almost human sensitivity. In the pudgy Irishman's nimble hands, the scarred and rosin-dusty instrument moaned and wept. It pleaded with you, laughed at you, put a waltz in your heart. And it sang the sad blues. Marcus sawed a fiddle like no other man in the Uwharries. You had to speak well ahead of time to engage him for a party or a square dance.

Fiddling was about all Marcus was good for, though, the hill people said. He'd go to barn raisings, log rollings, corn shuckings, and other hard-work activities, but mostly he went just to fiddle whenever there was a lull in the proceedings.

His uncommon passion for fiddling became legendary. His repertoire seemed endless. His fiddle could wear out dozens of dancers in succession while he was still warming up. Accompanists fell like flies by the wayside. Whenever his exhausted audience finally quit and went home and he still had a lot of good fiddling energy to release, Marcus would wander out alone, often in the wee hours of the morning, to the Marks graveyard. There, amid the pines and the honeysuckle beside Stony Run Creek, he would sit on the stone wall and fiddle for another hour to the tombstones glistening in the moonlight.

"That golden fiddle of Marcus O'Malley's could just about wake up the dead and make them shuffle their feet," devoted fans said.

Apparently one time it did just that.

The festivities had scarcely gotten off the ground one Saturday night before the people departed the country dance ahead of a threatening rainstorm. Marcus spent a restless night because he still had a lot of good fiddling raging inside him. The next morning he walked to the shack of his sidekick, Pete Maudlin, who sometimes accompanied him on the banjo. He downed a slug from Pete's whiskey jug.

"Pete," he said, "I feel like there's some people over at the Marks House wanting me to come play for them. Just feel it in my bones. I gotta go. Come along with me."

Fiddle case under his arm, Marcus strode out the door. Pete, red-eyed and unsteady, picked up his banjo and followed the fiddler to the Marks House, situated on a rise of ground near the main wagon road off to one side of the tiny village.

A community landmark for decades, the Marks House was a two-story log dwelling, spacious and comfortable, entirely adequate for the large Marks family and their occasional boarders. The big living room had seen many a square dance and quilting bee. Everyone within a radius of a dozen miles or more had enjoyed the renowned hospitality of the Marks House because of the conviviality of its proprietor, who never claimed to operate a hotel. He simply offered meals and temporary lodging to the hungry and shelterless. Adolphus Marks loved to tell about the Governors and their Ladies who had been his guests, and especially about a charming royal couple from the "old country."

On this bright Sunday morning Marcus and Pete found the Marks House deserted and strangely quiet. They knocked and hallooed, but received no response. So they went on inside and sat in the large parlor, an act not considered a serious breach of country manners. Marcus sat on the organ stool and warmed up his fiddle with a few lively tunes. Then he tightened a string or two, rubbed rosin against the bow hair, and sawed away, releasing the volley of music bottled up inside him since the previous evening.

The tunes frolicked out of the Irishman's fiddle and romped around the room. The music—sad, saucy, melancholy, and waltzy—would have held you spellbound, for it came from an instrument in the hands of a master.

Pete watched hopefully for an opening, then laid his unwrapped banjo aside. No use even trying to accompany Marcus when he lost himself so deeply and passionately in his music as he did now. Pete slouched in a comfortable rocker, tired eyelids drooping, and gazed into the fireplace.

Then he jerked erect. He stood up and cocked his ear as a new sound came to him above the fiddling. Footsteps sounded overhead —two pairs of footsteps, the heavier steps of a man and the lighter ones of a woman. There was rhythm in those steps. Then he knew. The foot movements were those of dancers. Two partners were dancing on the floor upstairs.

He touched Marcus to rouse him from his fiddling passion and nodded toward the ceiling. Marcus lowered the volume of his playing and listened. He, too, heard the steps and recognized the sound of experts dancing in perfect time with his playing. He nodded for Pete to go up and see who the dancers were.

But then both men turned their ears attentively as new sounds came from above. The dancers seemed to be moving toward the head of the stairs. After a few seconds Pete whispered, "They're coming down the stairs."

The dancers descended slowly on the stairs, as if they were lovers reluctant to leave the seclusion of the dim stairway. Occasionally a board creaked under their feet. Step by slow step the dancers descended, still keeping time with the music. They were at the bottom steps now. Marcus ended his tune with a flourish and turned to compliment the dancers on their footwork.

But he and Pete saw no one. They heard nothing—except their own excited breathing. Just silence and a mantle of strangeness. The

The Fiddler's Ghost Dancers   93

dancing had ceased along with the music. There were no scurrying footsteps, no opening or closing doors, no creaking boards, no rustle of clothing or patter of voices.

"They must've gone back up the steps before we saw them," Pete moaned.

Both men galloped up the steps and looked carefully in all the rooms. They found no one. They went back downstairs and searched the house inside and out, still without luck.

"But we both heard them," Marcus scowled. "I know dancing when I hear it. That was perfect dancing. I know there were dancers up there, and they came down those stairs. I heard them. But they just vanished in thin air right here."

"Maybe they was just thin air all the time," Pete wailed.

"I never heard of the Marks House being ha'nted, but I'm beginnin' to believe it," Marcus said.

Slowly Marcus returned the fiddle to its position under his chin and drew the bow over the strings. Pete wondered if his friend weren't in a spell or trance. Melody, golden and jubilant, winged around the room and floated into every crevice of the old house. Marcus' head drooped over the fiddle, and his eyes half-closed as he drew out the graceful notes.

What was it he had said about feeling that someone wanted him to come to the Marks House and play?

The dancing overhead began anew, apparently in the same spot. Pete glanced at Marcus, but Marcus appeared deeply lost in his music. Again the dancers, a light one and a heavier one, tripped lightly and deftly around the upstairs floor before they danced to the stairs and descended slowly toward the living room. Again they appeared to hesitate momentarily before coming all the way. This time Pete stood with his back against the wall so that he had an unimpeded view of the area and could see to the landing where the stairs turned. He saw no one.

Twice more, while Pete cowered silently against the wall, Marcus fiddled in total absorption, and the ghost couple danced leisurely from the upstairs room down to the bottom of the stairs. As Marcus put a fancy finale on his tune, the dancing ceased, and all was quiet. Pete saw no sign of any living or moving thing. Nor did he hear anything. Never was there any sound of footsteps going back up the stairs.

Then the Marks family, and a large one it was, came home from church, and for a few moments the house echoed with noise, chatter, and questions. Old Mr. Marks demanded to know why the two men were there and what was going on. Pete stammered into an explanation about something mysteriously pulling Marcus over here to play for the invisible dancers on the stairway. They scoffed at his words, and the bedlam of jabbering resumed until Pete frantically waved them to silence as he saw Marcus lift his fiddle into position again. He motioned for them to be quiet and pointed to his ear and then to the ceiling.

Marcus was oblivious of everything in the room now. He concentrated solely on his fiddle. The haunting melody with its intense emotional impact left the listeners spellbound. Some of the women dabbed at their eyes and sniffed. All were visibly touched at the striking beauty of the tune.

From upstairs the dancing commenced quickly. Deft feet touched softly on the floor over their heads. Obviously there was rhythm and skill in the footwork which kept perfect time with the music.

The Marks clan glanced about to see who could have gone upstairs to dance. But no one was missing. As the dancing gradually moved to the stairs and descended to the point where the dancers should have been visible but were not, the family stared at each other in amazement. Several of them stood so near the stairs they could have reached out and touched the dancers had they been touchable.

When the sounds of the dancing faded with the last fiddle note, the Markses plied Pete with questions he was unable to answer.

Several people ran upstairs to investigate, while others searched downstairs. Pete tried to tell them it was useless.

Then Pete saw Marcus inexorably move his fiddle to his chin. The fiddler's automatic mannerism—a slow stretching of his head up and around to relieve the stiffness—seemed to suggest that this would be Marcus' last fiddle tune for the occasion.

So it proved to be. Despite the human spectators lining their pathway, the ghost dancers began performing as usual. One of the young men impulsively dashed up to the stairway landing. He neither saw nor felt anything, only heard the dancing feet go past him on to the bottom of the stairs. When they reached the bottom, they stopped with the music. One or two witnesses said they thought they heard a faint laugh—a tired, happy, contented laugh—perhaps from a woman who had danced until she could dance no more.

Marcus came back to his senses nervously, asking questions and looking at his hands. He claimed that after the first tune he had had no control over his hands, that something had just started him playing and then stopped him, without any foreknowledge of the piece he would play. The people, whoever they were, seemed to have drawn him there especially to play for them until they grew tired of dancing.

Marcus continued to play his fiddle until he was a very old man. Through the years people came to recognize one peculiarity about his playing. On infrequent occasions—and only when he played dancing music—something akin to a trance would settle over the fiddler. His head would drop low on his instrument, his eyes almost close, and he would become oblivious of everything except his fiddle and his tenuous contact with an unknown entity. And the music his bow pulled from the scarred, rosin-dusty fiddle was rapturous and heavenly and wonderful for dancing.

But it was music that neither Marcus nor his audience had ever heard before.

THE GHOSTS IN THE BIG BLACK CLOUD

Pincus brown plowed through the corn with his mule, Old Beck. Just ahead, four children thinned the row corn and used their rough hoe blades to chop the wiry grass from amid the tangle of rocks and roots of the new-ground field. They had had their noon meal and rest an hour before and were now getting back in stride for another long afternoon of hoeing and plowing in the stump-studded field.

The muscles of the children, all teen-agers or better, were hardened from wielding the hoe blades, and their hands were creased from gripping the knotty homemade handles. Sweat popped out on their faces, hidden from the hot sun under the hand-sewn bonnets of the girls and the ragged straw hats of the boys.

The midday summer sun seared and irritated. They could see ripples of heat rise from the hot, dry earth. The dark green leaves of the knee-high corn were beginning to shrivel from lack of moisture. The plow and the hoes kicked up eddies of dust. Old Beck snorted in disgust.

On the next round, Pincus stopped even with the children, and they all took a drink of spring water from a jug brought from the house quite some distance away.

"Lookit that cloud, Pa," one of the boys said, pointing to the west. "Maybe rain, huh?"

They looked.

There, rolling slowly over the treetops toward them from the west, came a dark and threatening cloud which looked almost like a rain cloud. Yet there was a difference. This cloud hugged the ground and sifted through the trees, covering everything.

After his experienced eye had studied the cloud for an instant, Pincus said, "Looks like rain for sure. We'd better take out and head for the house."

He had begun unhitching the mule, and the children had dropped their hoes, when the fringes of the cloud reached them. At first it appeared to be gray wisps of smoke, or fog, or thick mist. But in less than a moment it had enveloped them in darkness blacker than the darkest night.

The children screamed and shouted hysterically. Pincus fought to keep a clear head himself.

"This way," he shouted. "Come here. Come to the sound of my voice. All of you gather here and hold hands."

Feeling his way carefully around the alarmed mule, Pincus finished unhitching her and gave the animal a free rein.

"Listen," he barked to the youngsters. "I'll ride Old Beck. You all hold onto my feet and onto Beck's mane and tail and onto each other's hands. Old Beck knows the way to the barn. She'll lead us in."

Instinct guided Old Beck unerringly in the right direction. It was a strange procession that stumbled out of the field and felt its way gingerly along the pathway to the log barn.

Eyes were quite useless in the impenetrable cloak of blackness.

They huddled together in the barn and waited, expecting at any moment to feel torrents of rain slamming down on the roof, or to hear balls of hail pelting the roof like bullets, or to see jagged flashes of lightning cracking the total darkness.

When no precipitation came from the black cloud, they ventured back out to the edge of the barnyard and stood there, unable to see even their hands held up before their faces. The midnight blackness seemed to creep over them and through them in alternating waves of warm, dark layers so thick and velvety they could almost grasp a handful of the stuff.

What was this strange blackness, the children asked each other. Where did it come from? When would it leave? They had no answers, and their father was unable to explain the anomaly.

Then they saw the figures—ghostly white spectres in motion overhead, contrasting sharply with the surrounding blackness.

Pincus saw them first. "Looky here!" he shouted to the children. "Over this way and up high." From force of habit he raised his arm and pointed, although no one could see his outstretched arm.

One by one the children turned, looked, and stumbled around until their eyes caught the white shapes in bold relief against the pervading void. They gasped and screamed. They clutched each other and huddled together and called to their father to tell them what to do.

"What in tarnation is it, Pa?" the oldest boy squalled to his father. "I thought we wuz all gone blind till these white things commenced to wiggle up there. What is they, Pa? Is the airth coming to a end?"

But Pincus Brown could do little to allay the fears of his children, for he was just as stunned and befuddled as they at this magic in the sky. The children listened and looked, engrossed now that their initial fright had subsided.

From the stories they told of the sights they saw in that inky blackness, you would think that they had witnessed a whole history book full of famous personages parading in the dismal darkness over the barnyard.

They told of a uniformed soldier wearing a peculiar three-cornered hat, of a leader with curled white hair standing at the helm of a boat, of ship captains, Indian chiefs, and shepherds, of savages with spears, of kings and queens on their thrones.

Finally, the children said, the figures faded away, to be replaced moments later by a panoramic view of the heavens, showing the moon, planets, stars, and other celestial bodies. There were vehicles with people in them shooting to and from bright star-like objects in the black void over the barnyard. In any direction they looked, these starry objects were visible. It was about like looking at the heavens on a clear wintry night, they said, except that here they were much closer.

Suddenly a shriek of wonder and surprise came from Pincus Brown. One of the white, human-like ghost-figures had captured his attention, and his voice sounded as if he were following it around the barnyard. He cried joyously to the figure again and again.

"It's Maw, it's Maw!" Pincus Brown screamed. "Maw's up there! I can see her plain. Hey, Maw, it's me, Pincus, your son. Maw, look down here at me!"

The huddled children heard the quick footsteps of their father as he darted further out into the barnyard to wave and shout for the attention of a floating white shape which he believed to be his mother. They knew, from his many stories of his boyhood, about his devoted mother who had died when he was a fifteen-year-old boy on the Carolina frontier.

The Brown children cringed together in silent awe as they heard their father weep and sob, pleading in agonized tones for the image of his dear dead mother to look down and recognize him.

"Dear old Maw," he entreated brokenly, "won't you just look down at me once? You know I loved you and worshiped you. You know how I've thought lovingly about you every day since you left us. It's just so grand to be able to look on your face again, Maw. Won't you just give me a sign that you know I'm here? Won't you, please?

"You're an angel, Maw, I know you are. Nothing but an angel could appear to me like this. Except the Good Lord, Himself. I know you're an angel, Maw, and I know I can see you plain. Why won't you look at me? Why, Maw? Won't you? Please do."

Pincus Brown kept talking like this for a long time to the ghostly image of his mother.

Finally, the image of his mother began to respond. He rejoiced and hallelujahed. Pincus called his children by name and bade them

come and look upon their grandmother, and she upon them. Proudly he introduced them and told the children that here was the wonderful person he had told them so much about.

"Maw, you used to tell me you'd see me in glory. Is this what you meant? Is it, Maw? Is this glory? Then I want to stay with you in glory forever. Don't leave us now that you've come back, Maw. Please don't. But if you can't stay here with us, then take me back with you. Right now. I'm ready to go. The chillun and their maw can look after the farm here without me. They'll be all right. So, I'm ready to go with you, back to glory. Take me right now. I'm holding up my hands to you."

The white image of the woman came closer and bent forward, her hands outstretched. Other figures and hands pressed around her to assist.

Pincus Brown began to rise.

The children saw their father rising in the air.

Instinctively, they clutched at him and held to his clothing.

"No, Paw, no, you can't leave us!" squalled the older boy. "We ain't lettin' you go nowhere. Help me hold 'im!"

They held onto their father for dear life. All the children tugged and clawed and pulled at their father. Occasionally his feet rose waist high, as the four children frantically clung to his legs, resisting the pull from above. And all the while, Pincus Brown kicked and screamed for them to turn him loose so he could go on and join his maw in glory.

Abruptly, patches of light began to chase away some of the awful blackness. Glimmers of gray appeared overhead, and blades of light sliced the darkness. When the streaks became more frequent, they knew the black cloud was moving on. It left as suddenly as it had come, with wisps and tufts of gray, smoky mist bobbing along the trailing edge.

But one ashen blob of mist lingered, even as the bright, sultry sunlight of midafternoon blazed down upon them again. Several hands of the misty substance protruded from the small gray cloud, clasping the hands and arms of Pincus Brown, seeking to pull him into it. The children still swung and dangled from the feet and legs of their airborne father, dragging their own feet in the barnyard dirt to impede the progress of the slowly drifting cloud.

Then the small cloud apparently decided it could dawdle no longer, and the hands released their grip on Pincus Brown. He fell on the flank of a haystack, the children sprawling around him. The vagrant blob of cloud hastened to catch up with the masses of gray-blackness now sifting through the trees on the far side of the clearing.

Pincus Brown lay in the hay on his stomach and sobbed for a few minutes. The two younger children were crying too. It took Pincus a long time to stand and unwind himself and collect his senses. He kept turning and looking around, dazed and unbelieving.

The next day he made inquiries about the cloud throughout the Uwharries. No other family had seen the weird black cloud. People stared at him in pity when he related his experience.

After a few days of excited jabbering about the occurrence, some of the children wondered if it hadn't been a dream after all. References by the neighbors and kinfolks to the event as a dream gave this idea to outsiders, and this was the impression formed by most hearers of the tale—that the ghost cloud was merely an especially-vivid dream experienced by a member of the Brown family, whose enthusiasm about it had infected the others. For years the "Brown Family's Dream" remained a subject of derision in the community.

But Pincus Brown never for an instant doubted the reality of the experience in the big black cloud. He died a stooped old man, firmly convinced that he had seen his mother in the cloud and that he would go now to be with her again—in glory.

Everyone who knew Pincus was satisfied that he did.

THE GALLOPING GHOST

JOHN EHRINGER was a middle-aged engineer when he came into the Uwharries the second time, back in the days when the state first began rebuilding and hard-surfacing roads in this section of the Piedmont. A versatile roadbuilder, he did everything from the original surveying to purchasing the right-of-way, to supervising the grading, to filing the final applications for approval. On each project he camped in a tent or trailer at the job to exercise personal control over every move along the way. That's why his jobs turned out to be technically superior to the jobs of others.

Ehringer met an unnatural obstacle on a half-mile stretch of new road through a gentle Uwharrie valley. All had progressed normally up to that point—and did so beyond it, for that matter. Only along that half-mile-long section of road did Ehringer encounter a situation for which even his amazing engineering background had not prepared him.

There the path of the new road departed from the old secondary road it had been following and took a short cut across country to avoid some winding curves. Along most of the short cut, the new road followed the bed of an old sawmill wagon road, heavily used in its day, but later abandoned.

Ehringer first heard the noise while surveying along the short-cut route. One night he and his helper camped right in the middle of the old wagon road, where it was clear and dry. They were jarred out of their bedrolls when the noise came—the distinct sound of galloping hoofbeats and the creak of saddle leather under the weight of a rider. Before the men could move, the sound of the galloping horseback rider approached, passed directly over them, and faded out down the lonely road. Shakily, they scrambled up, asking each other if the horse and rider hadn't jumped over them. But neither had seen any such thing. Directly, the galloping horse came back, again sounding as if it passed right on top of them. The noise lost itself in the direction from which it had originally come.

Both men were flabbergasted. But after discussing the occurrence at length, they concluded that the sound must have come from a hard-packed, much-traveled road not far away. The next morning they were startled to find fresh hoofprints in the eroded red soil of the old roadbed. They knew these tracks had not been there the day before. Remembering two obstacles blocking the road, one a barbed-wire fence and the other a huge fallen tree, they went to check. The hoofmarks continued unbroken, through and under the log and the fence—as if those barriers had not been there at all.

Ehringer's trained and logical mind rebelled at the physical evidence. His helper, Jernigan, scoffed, refusing to give credence to the hoofmarks.

"That what we heered last night was a hoss, all right," he drawled. "But Gawd knows, you know it couldn'ta left them tracks—not on through the fence and the log. Somebody is jest playin' tricks on us, Boss."

Though their work progressed beyond that point, they came back at dusk and camped on the old roadbed again to listen for the noise. But they did not hear it that night. Weeks later they were back that way checking on property ownership, and they camped again on the old road. This time a jovial farmer of the community joined them, and they sat up late talking around a flickering little campfire. Suddenly the galloping horse noise descended upon them and passed over them and then faded in the distance.

"It'll come back," Ehringer said. "And when it does, I'll be

The Galloping Ghost   105

standing right here in the middle of this old road to see what happens."

Jernigan howled objections, told the boss he was crazy, and backed well off the road into some bushes to watch.

But the farmer spat and came to stand beside Ehringer. "I'll stand with you," he said, "because I know what'll happen."

In a few minutes the noise returned, sounding exactly like a furiously-running horse carrying a heavy rider. It passed by them, or over them, or through them. Then the thudding hoofbeats receded into the black night. They neither saw nor felt anything as it passed.

"Somethin' blowed the fire as that noise passed," Jernigan reported. "I seed the flame bend over low like it wuz blowed by a breeze. 'Cept there wasn't no breeze."

The farmer shed a little light. "I can hear the same noise coming from over this way some nights when I'm sitting out in the cool on my porch or in the yard. People around here have heard that horse galloping over this old road for years. Been going on so long they don't pay it no mind any more. 'Course, it always interests a stranger. Don't ever hurt nobody. Jest keeps on a-galloping. Always at night around bedtime or after. Some folks claim to have heard it at midnight, and I guess they have. It's supposed to be the ghost of a mean old scoundrel who used to shoot and rob people along here. Old Uncle Zeb Sasser knows about him. If you want to find out, go and see Uncle Zeb."

At the first opportunity, Ehringer looked up Uncle Zeb at his crumbling farmhouse a mile from the scene of the noise. He made known his job and his business there and asked for an explanation of the ghostly galloping. Stooped with age, bearded and grizzled, Uncle Zeb hobbled up close, clutching his gnarled cane. All his hair was white, and his eyes pierced Ehringer like blue icicles.

"Son, you go disturbing that old roadbed any and you may be in for trouble. That ghost has got to gallop, and that old road there is his favorite place. Might be you oughta build your road somewheres else and not take the risk." He settled his fragile bones on the edge of the porch, and his eyes roved the distant Uwharrie ridges, where crows cawed at an intruding hawk.

"Yep, I can tell you about the ghost. Buller was his name. Buller. He was a bull all right. A mean 'un. Owned a huge farm over here. Lot of land and timber. Big plantation, too. Used to be slaves on it. He was well-off and had as much as any man should ask for. But he was greedy. Always wanted more. And he wasn't careful how he got it. Many people he cheated outta their land and homes and crops. If farmers around his land refused to sell out to him dirt cheap, he'd cause them trouble, ruin them some way, or burn them out to make them sell.

"For years he was a magistrate, the only law in these parts. If you ever got in debt to him, look out; he'd come git you and make you work long and hard on his farm to settle the debt. Any time he got low on workers, he'd go out and arrest people, for hardly any excuse at all, and drive them back to his farm to work as punishment. Some who objected and resisted were slugged and beaten to death.

"He always rode a big black stallion, and he carried a shotgun, had a pistol and a knife at his belt and a long whip in his hand. He'd ride by and whip his hands in the field sometimes. Or he'd go get a man, bind his hands, tie a lead rope from him to the saddle, and make him trot behind the horse. When the man got tired and fell, Buller would keep his horse trottin' right on and drag the man over the dirt and rocks. They say he even killed some this way.

"In his old age he took to robbing people. Outright highway robbery. There was a lot of traveling on that road, by salesmen and merchants and haulers and other people with goods and money. Some camped at his spring by the road, and some lodged at his home. He robbed them all. Most regular travelers learned about him and wouldn't let night catch them anywhere near Buller land.

Then, only strangers fell into his trap. But he got lots of them. Even in daylight he'd accuse the more unprotected wagons of trespassing, and he'd climb aboard them and take what he wanted, cuffing the women and children out of his way."

Uncle Zeb talked on, but Ehringer wasn't listening. Zeb's last words had awakened memories, and Ehringer contemplated them in the light of the old man's story. He knew it was fantastic. But surely it must be true. This must have been the situation he and his parents had gotten into when he was a child.

He remembered his parents telling the story many times. At dark one night Tom and Cora Ehringer and their two small children, John and Patsy, stopped their heavy wagon at a spring in sight of a big farmhouse in the Uwharries. They were worn out from the day's drive, and the team sagged wearily from pulling the wagon since sunup. Rather than risk trying to find another campsite, they pitched camp there. As they huddled around a campfire eating a meager supper, a thickset man with a beefy face and cold eyes galloped up. He greeted them, saying they were on his land, and asked them many questions. An ominous glint lighted his eyes as he left abruptly and rode away into the night.

Meanwhile, a local traveler, chancing to pass, stopped with a terse message: "Get going. This is Buller land. He robs and kills people here. If he hasn't robbed you yet, he will before the night's over. Hitch up and drive all night if you have to. Just get away from here while you can."

The Ehringers left at once, not stopping to put out their fire. They had driven several miles through the cold night when a group of mounted men overtook them. Buller headed the group. His harsh voice hailed them to a stop.

In the dim lantern light at the front of the wagon, Cora Ehringer cringed in fear against her husband, who gripped the reins with nervous hands. Buller's men held the bridles of the horses to prevent Tom Ehringer from trying to escape by lashing his jaded animals into a run. The children awoke and began whimpering inside the wagon.

Buller told them bluntly that they could either give up their gold and whatever goods and cash they had, or he and his henchmen would kill every one of them, throw their bodies in the river, and take their money anyway.

Ehringer had no choice but to submit to the outrage to safeguard the lives of his family. He tossed out a small bag of gold coins. But that did not satisfy Buller. He held a gun on them while his henchmen took the lantern and searched the wagon, taking whatever they wanted.

Suddenly Buller told an accomplice to hand him one of the children. With his left hand, he grasped John's ankle and lifted him so his head dangled about even with the saddle horn. With his right hand, Buller slowly cocked a big pistol and placed the muzzle against the child's head. His finger began to squeeze the trigger.

Cora Ehringer screamed piercingly and tried to fight her way off the wagon seat to get to Buller and her child. But Buller's man on the wagon cuffed her and held her back.

Buller laughed in obvious enjoyment. He spurred his horse forward, held the dangling boy out like a sack of meal, and dropped him on the lap of the cringing mother.

"Take the brat," he bellowed. "I'd just as soon've killed him, like I'll kill all of you if you breathe a word about this to anybody. Now git, and don't ever come back!"

They had remained silent until years later. Now, John Ehringer realized that what had been a hazy, dreamlike recollection all these years really had occurred, right here along this road on Buller land.

He heard Uncle Zeb talking again.

"In the last few years of his life, old man Buller seemed to repent some. He was still mean and ornery, but maybe he had a touch of remorse too. He couldn't sleep at night. His mind was so burdened and his conscience so heavy that he couldn't rest. So, about every night, he saddled the stallion and rode lickety-split up and down that old road through the woods. Folks claim he did it to soothe his conscience and to wear himself out so he could sleep. Kept doing it right up till he died. Must have been forty years ago or longer. They never did learn who done it, but one night a bushwhacker's bullet zinged out of the trees and killed the old man while he was riding along that old wagon road. He wasn't found till the next day. There weren't many at the funeral, either.

"Ever since then, people have heard this ghostly galloping on the old road at night. They claim it's Buller's ghost, still burdened by all the evil he's done, out riding to clear his troubled conscience. It used to create a big commotion among people hereabouts. A few people even claimed the ghost robbed them of their money. I don't know about that. Maybe it did. Then people gradually stopped using that road, and there weren't any more complaints about it. Now people here have gotten used to the galloping and just don't let it bother them none. The way we figure it, that ghost will keep on riding till eternity before it can make up for all the wrong Buller done.

"But you'd better be careful if you're going to try to rebuild that road. Buller's ghost ain't gonna like having its riding place tore up. It might try to stop you. If you've got to build it there, go ahead, but watch out for that ghost."

Ehringer went on with his road as planned. He wasn't about to let a ghost stop his work. Besides, he had a personal interest in this one.

Some of the men cutting right-of-way heard the ghost next. They had been forewarned by Jernigan, but they were skeptical until the unseen horse galloped through their midst, scattering them squalling right and left. Before they could collect themselves and their wits, the rapidly thudding hoofbeats thundered back through. There were no skeptics now.

As the work progressed, Ehringer and the workmen heard the

galloping ghost on several occasions. It seemed to ignore the changes in the road and the cumbersome machinery in the way. None of the old roadbed remained now. The new grade had necessitated cutting down several feet into the old road throughout much of its length, as well as filling in a low place or two.

Finally the new road was on grade, and packers firmed it with crushed stone for a stabilizing base. Still the thudding hoofbeats could be heard, sounding each time as if they came right down the middle of the road.

A few workmen began missing coins and money from their pockets. No big amounts, for no one had much money anyway, just pocket change and a bill or two. Ehringer himself missed a few bills from his wallet. No culprit was ever found.

Ehringer stayed so busy that several days passed before he got back to the site of the old wagon road once the surfacing crews had passed that point. One night about bedtime, he and a workman built a small fire on the shoulder of the new road and sat down to wait. They were joined by the jovial farmer who had stood with Ehringer to face the mysterious noise there months before.

Talk waned, and the hooting of owls in the black forest lulled them into drowsiness before the galloping ghost appeared. But it came as usual, whisking past them at a furious gallop down the middle of the new road. All of them noticed a distinct difference in the sound. Gone was the soft thudding, plopping sound of hooves striking yielding soil. Now the noise had the clear, hard, brittle ring of hooves clicking solidly against something hard—like a paved road.

That road has been rebuilt and resurfaced again and again. Each time the crews of workmen have heard strange hoofbeats in the night. They say the ghost of old man Buller still rides along the ancient highway. If you want to see for yourself, go there and park, some night, and listen carefully for the sound of the galloping ghost. It might, however, be wise to leave your money at home.

SAMBO'S WOODS

THE WOODS AROUND Sambo's grave were changing. Rupert Baucom knew it for a fact now. He could feel it. Moreover, he could see it. A trained woodsman all his life, he noted even the most subtle variation in these woods which he had known intimately since childhood. Not only was it change that he sensed, but transformation. And he knew that there was more—much more—to come, here on Gourdvine Creek in the Uwharries.

At first, the realization puzzled and troubled him. Why were the woods changing? Why this particular portion of the woods, deep within the forest? What combination of natural causes could trigger this botanical transfiguration?

Or were they natural causes at all?

Each time he walked the mile or so from his farm to the lonely spot deep in the forests of the Gourdvine, Rupert became more convinced that the oaks and the gums, the honeysuckle vines and the bramble thickets, were turning into an equatorial rain forest of tropical vegetation.

Tropics? Equator? Yes, maybe that was it! Guinea was near the equator. Of course! Guinea had been Sambo's home.

His mind raced back to Sambo. Though it had been five years since Sambo's death, Rupert could still see him as plain as day. Big, black, brawny Sambo, with bluntly-chiseled face, expressive eyes, and a heart as big as his back was stout. He had been fearless as a mountain lion, loyal as a pet dog. But he had been a pathetically lonely man, who had never been able to adjust to being snatched from the hot jungles of his native Africa and buffeted to these bleak

Uwharrie hills. He had withered and died here, of homesickness, forever yearning for his native land.

Rupert had first seen Sambo on the battlefield at Chickamauga amid whining rifle balls and roaring cannons. Rupert had been scuttling on all fours behind a barrier of rocks and stumps when he came upon a giant black man groaning and groveling on his face in the bloody dirt, close to a dying white boy in a lieutenant's uniform. Rupert paused to help them.

"Get your damn head down," the youngster rasped laboriously. "Me and Sam don't want your carcass falling all over us when them bullets riddle you."

Rupert said that he had come to help, that maybe he could patch them up some until the medics came.

"I'm past help," the boy gasped, blood on his mouth. "But see about Sambo. Stop his bleeding. Save him if you can. Sambo's my manservant and a good 'un. Not afraid of Hell itself. But he don't speak English much 'cause he ain't more'n four-five years out of Guinea. Do what you can to save him, and I'll give him to you. Just one thing: set him free when this war's over. Will you?"

Rupert said that he would. He began improvising a tourniquet for the nasty shrapnel wound in the black man's thigh. Sambo stirred and started to resist, but then he grasped the situation and tried to co-operate with his benefactor.

The lieutenant rambled incoherently. In a weakening voice he asked if Rupert had ever heard the wild geese honking in the misty Georgia marshlands or the waves breaking on the Georgia shore. Rupert replied that he had not, that he was a hill man and lived in a place where there had never been any shore or ocean. But wild geese and ducks? He could tell him a thing or two about them. But the Georgia boy wasn't listening. His chalky face and staring eyes were locked on the buzzards circling far overhead.

Sambo recovered rapidly, understood that he had a new master, and accompanied Rupert through the remainder of the war. After the surrender and demobilization, they trudged back to the farm on the Gourdvine. By this time Rupert liked the idea of having a man-servant around, so he never told Sambo that he was free or that the war had been fought to liberate him and his kind.

Each learned a little more of the other's language, and they were able to communicate. Rupert resumed farming, and Sambo did most of the heavy work. He attacked all his work with an energetic zeal that surprised Rupert. But the black man worked for a purpose. Almost every day he'd ask the same question: "Marster, when I make you rich, will you send me back to Guinea?"

Rupert always said that he would, and Sambo worked ever harder.

But Sambo was a lonely man with a chasm of emptiness widening within him. He was a man out of his element, floundering, unable to adjust. He cringed away from the strange white people who oc-casionally stopped to visit Rupert. In the fields he would pause, his face hopeful, while his eyes raked the horizon. At the end of each day's work, he would pace the yard, muttering strange incantations, the meaning of which only he knew. Often at night Rupert would wake to hear Sambo in the adjoining room, thrashing about and gib-bering in his strange tongue.

One summer day, three years after his arrival at the Gourdvine, Sambo unhooked his mule from the plow and came to the house to face Rupert. He had an unusually faraway look in his eyes. He said the spirits were calling him from Africa, and he could stand it no longer. He'd have to go. Then he made a strange request.

He said that his people had strong feelings for the dead. They thought that the living should never walk over the dead—or even very near them—because the footsteps would wake up the dead and cause them to have to die all over again. He asked Rupert to bury him deep in the woods and let nobody near his grave.

Then he said that his young Georgia master had told him that Africa, where Guinea was, was almost on the other side of the world. So he wanted to be buried face downward, since yearning that way might get him back to Guinea quicker. He said that it might take him a hundred years to get back where he had come from, but that he'd be yearning all the time.

Sambo died. Rupert lugged his body by muleback into the wilds of the Gourdvine at the back of his property and buried him on his face. He spread the word among his neighbors that, for special reasons of his own, he didn't want any hunting or moonshining or even any walking around on that part of his property. There was some grumbling, but most of his neighbors respected his request and stayed away. From that day on, Sambo's section of the Gourdvine was seldom visited.

Except by Rupert. He came because of his fondness for the big black man, who had been kind and generous and companionable beyond the requirements of his servitude. Rupert always came quietly and stood reverently near—but not too near—the grave, musing and reflecting about the strange man who lay there on his face under the sod and forest litter. He hoped that the black man would someday get back to Guinea. He hoped fervently that he would. As he continued his farming in subsequent months, Rupert would walk to the grave every few days to stand there and yearn awhile. Yearn? Yes, he was joining the dead man in yearning for his passage back to Guinea.

Two years passed before he sensed the presence of the other yearners. He couldn't see them. He couldn't hear them or touch them. But he knew they were there. Their presence became more evident with the passing of time.

The knowledge did not alarm Rupert. It seemed fitting that the dead man had somehow summoned help. The collective yearning energized the atmosphere, and Rupert could detect faint vibrations and pulsations in the air. He assumed that these were what enabled him to sense and visualize the other yearners.

What he sensed was more of Sambo's kind—big black people with sad faces and mournful eyes and with highly developed yearning powers. There were weird medicine men who used colorful props and unusual gesticulations in their incantations for Sambo; there were tom-tom beaters, hand-clappers, jog-stepping dancers, and chanters of assorted mumbo-jumbo. Rupert did not understand what tenuous contact enabled him to identify them. That they came from Guinea to help Sambo yearn, Rupert had no doubt. Hadn't Sambo said something about the spirits calling him from Africa? Though they were aware of his presence, the spirits appeared not to resent his being there. Perhaps they knew that he, too, yearned for Sambo.

About five years after the death of Sambo, the yearning had developed into a surging but silent crescendo. This was when Rupert first noticed that an acre or two around the grave was turning tropical. He kept close watch through a cycle of seasons as the transition became more pronounced. The bitter Uwharrie winter, with the temperature nudging zero, failed to affect the burgeoning vegetation around Sambo's grave. It remained colorful, lush, and steamy the year round. The area beyond the border was filled with dull, nondescript shrubs and undergrowth, but the interior gleamed with exotic blossoms, rubber plants with waxen foliage, ferns and bamboo, palm and fruit trees. The very ground, which had been clay before, had turned to sand.

More surprises came.

As the seasons passed, Rupert began to half-sense, half-see, strange animals and birds, all foreign to the Uwharries. He could identify lions, leopards, wild boars, antelopes, hippopotami, snakes, and crocodiles. He recognized the egret, the pelican, and the parrot.

No matter what the conditions outside, as soon as Rupert shouldered through the perimeter hedge, he always found the climate hot and moist. Balmy breezes caressed his face. He saw fish leaping in the stream. Sea life abounded along the beach.

One day he lay down to rest on a stretch of clean white sand.

Soon, the sound of waves rocking in on the shore lulled him into drowsiness. Strange cries of jungle creatures woke him. Hungry, he picked and ate some of the bananas, grapes, and wild fruit that grew in abundance. Suddenly it began to rain furiously, but Rupert remained dry and comfortable under the thick foliage. Moments later, as he left to walk home, he found the forest leaves bone dry and crinkly, and the fields and roads powdery with dust. When he got home, he heard a faint braying from the barn and found the old mule looking like a dirty rag wrapped around a bony skeleton—as if she hadn't been fed in days, though he could remember feeding her shortly before he left to go into the woods.

In subsequent weeks, he began going to Sambo's grave more often and staying longer. It was pleasant there, with plenty of food, no work, and no worry. Now he left the stable door open so that the old mule could get out and forage if she became hungry.

Visitors to the isolated farm seldom found Rupert there, and they surmised that he must be off in the woods moping around the grave of that Negro he'd brought home from the war. There were things that some of them—hunters mainly—wanted to ask him about those woods. Puzzling things. Despite Rupert's request that everyone stay away from that part of the woods, hunters sometimes could not keep their hounds from chasing a fox or coon into the area.

When they did, strange things happened. The dogs would suddenly quit the chase and come whimpering back to the hunters' lanterns. But why? The hounds would yelp freely under the stars until the quarry headed up the Gourdvine to the spot where the man from Guinea lay. Then their voices would die, only to be resumed, moments later, in a subdued tone—not one of joy. At that point the baying was more like the crying of a man over the grave of his brother. Soon the hunters realized that it was useless to continue the hunt when their dogs chased the quarry into Sambo's Woods. And nobody wanted to make an on-the-spot check to see what the dogs found there in the woods.

Other reports, many of them from strangers and newcomers who blundered into the area, told of startling glimpses and sounds of most unusual creatures. One man said he had seen a snake twenty feet long. Others who got close to Sambo's sanctuary claimed that they had heard the roar of a lion and the thunder of a hippo. Those who reached the perimeter of Sambo's Woods claimed that they had been met by a curtain of heavy rainfall, or by a dense cloud of fog or stifling steam, or by a barricade of jungle thorns too prickly to penetrate. There were tales of dreadful afflictions—sleeping sickness, malaria, and other tropical maladies—contracted by persons who tarried too long around Sambo's domain.

A few men in the community became embittered over the situation and voiced hostilities toward Rupert. How long would these spooks continue to hang around the Gourdvine and scare people away? But they could never find Rupert at home any more to inquire about these things. Most people kept their peace and rationalized that Sambo's Woods were so far out of the way that nobody had any business going there anyway. Rupert's old house sagged, and the field and forest clutched it.

The years rolled by. Many of the oldsters died off, and younger people took over the farms. They brought change and improvement. Progress began to sweep into the hills—electricity, new roads, new homes, mechanization.

One bright fall day the occupants of a new brick home stared hard at a ragged and ancient man who hobbled into their yard and surveyed the terrain with wide and incredulous eyes. He staggered around and around, looking . . . disbelieving.

"My home! Where is it? My house used to stand here. What have you done with it? I live here! Don't you understand? My barn, my well, my garden? What's happened to my place?"

His voice quavered and broke. It shrilled rustily, then plunged to a sob. Wildly-unfurling white beard and hair wreathed the old man's face, which was centered by a thin nose separating two cavernous eyes. His scrawny, bare arms and lower legs were those of a man bronzed by sea and sun. The shock of what he saw caused his head to twitch and his arms to jerk. He looked long at a sleek new car in the driveway.

"But I live here," he whispered. "I used to live here, and now it's all gone away."

A young man stepped close. "Mister, my folks have owned this farm for thirty years or longer. There used to be an old house and an outbuilding or two, but they rotted down and we cleared them away. Who are you, old man, and where have you been living since you left?"

But the ancient one appeared not to have heard. His limp frame drooped, and he turned and tottered back the way he had come.

The younger man kept pace with him for a step or two. "But where will you go? You're old and weak and sickly. Will you be all right? Have you any place to stay?"

The old man stopped and looked around and nodded. "Yes, I'll be all right. Yes, I have a place to go." Feebly, he limped on and soon crossed the field and vanished into the deep woods.

Within a few years, woodsmen brought reports that the tangle of perimeter hedge in the area of the Negro's grave had loosened up some and that the strangeness seemed to be leaving the place. One winter day hunters prowling through the wilds of the Gourdvine sloughed through thickets of strange, mottled foliage, which reminded them somewhat of huge hothouse plants losing their battle with the cold. Near a stream they crunched over white sand and brittle sea shells, littered with winter's leaves. There they found the white bones of a human skeleton, a few wisps of fabric, scraps of crinkled leather around the foot bones, and a tarnished brass buckle at the bottom of the rib cage.

Many years have passed. Visitors to Sambo's Woods no longer encounter obstacles, nor anything else to frighten or alarm them. Day and night, the hounds now make joyous music chasing their quarry freely all over the wilds of the Gourdvine.

It is reckoned that Sambo finally got back to Guinea, but no one knows for sure.

During World War II, a local soldier, familiar with the Sambo legend, spent some time in Guinea. He claims he saw there a huge, happy Negro man, obviously a leader among his people. Always at his side was an older, rangy, long-stepping white man, whose squinty eyes appeared to scan distant horizons. What attracted the soldier's attention most was the white man's voice—a slow nasal drawl very common around the Uwharrie Gourdvine community. When the white man spoke to the black giant, the soldier heard him say, among other things, respectfully, "Yes, Master Sambo."

THE HEAVY HITCHHIKER

Turbulence dogged Ephraim Tucker through life. It reached a peak in his latter years, when the old man, fierce and opinionated, involved himself in one controversy after another, alienating many people in the community, including his own family. It scarcely surprised the people of the Uwharries when this condition continued right on as if death had made very little difference. Some folks believe that Tucker's turbulence, even yet, may not be completely abated.

A prosperous farmer and a gristmill and lumber plant operator, Tucker had influence, and he likely could have had his way on most issues had not his personal habits and cantankerous ways offended people. His wife, Mavis, had put up with him somehow, though they warred constantly. Their only son, Bertrand, had grown into his mid-forties without marrying. He had always been a peculiar boy, eccentric, and a loner. He paid little attention to either parent, or to anyone else, for that matter.

The focal point of the latest controversy was old Rehobeth Church, in which Ephraim Tucker had been a leader most of his life. Ephraim thought that his way to run the church was the only way. Advancing age made him worse. His domination became intolerable. Splits developed in the church, and movements got under way to dispossess the old man of his authority. Several substantial members were ready to pull out and build themselves a new church, despite Ephraim's oft-repeated statement that he was remembering the church in his will and would leave it well fixed after he was gone. Most members would have settled for the latter.

About this time old Ephraim up and died. Fell dead suddenly one day while at work in his mill. His funeral was big and showy. As they lowered him into the red earth of the church cemetery, you could hear his widow agonizing for a mile. Bertrand displayed little emotion.

Dissension in the church had reached such proportions that Ephraim's death didn't heal the wounds. About half the congregation withdrew and built a new church over on the other side of the community. They called this church New Salvation. The widow Tucker, expressing a desire to make a fresh start and to get away from reminders of her husband's tyranny, joined the new church and contributed generously to its construction. Bertrand, however, remained loyal to old Rehobeth.

Nearly a year after Ephraim's death, Mose Tucker, a banker cousin of Ephraim's, arrived from Richmond with information about the decedent's will, which had been left with him a few years before. Ephraim had provided an adequate income for his wife and son, as well as lifetime residence in the Tucker home. The farm and all the property were to be sold and the proceeds given to "the church which my family attends and where all of us will be buried."

When Mose learned that there was a division in the church, that the widow attended the splinter church, intending to be buried there come what might, and that the son stood staunchly true to old Rehobeth, he closed his briefcase and drove his buggy back to Richmond. He told them to send him word when and if they ever got their church affiliation and burial arrangements straightened out so that he could settle the estate and give one of the churches its due.

The widow Tucker was wroth over her son's refusal to leave old Rehobeth and come to New Salvation. If he would come, she pleaded, it would be simple for them to dig up old Ephraim and move him, too; then the church could qualify for the gift. But Bertrand remained as unmoved as Gibraltar, saying if old Rehobeth was good enough for his father in life and death, then it was good enough for him. His mother could come back there, he suggested.

But the widow had found such happiness at New Salvation that she would never leave it, in life or in death, gift or no gift. And there the matter would have stood, had not the church members learned about the provisions of the will and joined in the fight. They knew that a gift like the Tucker estate would meet all the church's financial needs, as well as pay the preacher, for at least a generation to come. So the New Salvation members tried to persuade Bertrand to change his mind and join them, while the Rehobeth congregation tenaciously clung to him and tried to induce the widow to return.

One bright day a gaping hole appeared in the old Rehobeth graveyard where the coffin of Ephraim Tucker had been. When news of the grave-robbing circulated, Rehobeth members swarmed, hopping mad, to look at the empty grave. With Bertrand in their midst, they went to New Salvation and there found a fresh grave, in fact the only grave, in the new cemetery. The stone marker bore the name of Ephraim Tucker. Beside it, two additional plots had been laid off—one for Mavis Tucker, wife of Ephraim Tucker, and the other for Bertrand Tucker—so said the slabs of native slate. The Rehobeth hotheads would probably have dug Ephraim up right then and carried him back to his original resting place, had not some New Salvation members appeared with guns in their hands to discourage such an act. So the Rehobethans retreated and bided their time.

A few weeks later, in the middle of the night, two groups of men from the Rehobeth congregation worked stealthily and fast. One group exhumed the remains of Ephraim Tucker from the New Salvation graveyard, while the second group reopened the old grave at Rehobeth to receive him again. The maneuver succeeded, and the switch wasn't discovered until the following afternoon. By that time, Bertrand had laid off two additional grave plots beside his father's—one for himself and one for his mother. He was erecting the markers for them when his mother and a delegation from New Salvation arrived.

The widow Tucker called her son cruel and heartless. She begged him to reconsider and come to New Salvation. He refused and said he would listen no further to her rantings. Some of the men accompanying the widow had picks and shovels. They would have taken Ephraim's remains back with them, had it not been for the appearance of armed and ready Rehobeth men.

Two other grave-robbing switches occurred in succeeding months. How bloodshed was avoided is not understood. A few shots were fired, but apparently no one was hurt. On the last move, Rehobeth men brought their own security guard. While the diggers uncovered Ephraim's scarred coffin, in broad daylight this time, the guard ringed them with firearms at the ready to keep any interferers at bay. The same guards accompanied the party back to Rehobeth and watched over the replanting of Ephraim's remains at the Rehobeth cemetery. From then on, Rehobeth men kept vigil at the grave in shifts.

The explosive situation simmered for the next few weeks, ready to boil over into a blood-spilling feud. But then the widow Tucker collapsed from acute nervous frustration one day, and died the next. They held the funeral at New Salvation and buried her in the grave she had picked out beside the grave that had twice held her husband but was now empty.

Shortly thereafter, Bertrand's mind, never too stable, snapped, and henceforth he became a gibbering idiot who scavenged around the community day and night. The preachers at Rehobeth and New Salvation discussed Bertrand, and for a few Sundays they preached to their respective flocks soul-searing sermons about the poor man being a symbol of God's punishment, a great weight on the community's conscience, a blot and black mark branding the community for all to see, a living reminder of their sins during the grave-robbing period. Repentant families tried to make amends by offering to feed, clothe, and shelter Bertrand. But the crazed man, something less than an animal now, would have little of their handouts, not being able to recognize or understand offers of help. Somehow he seemed immune to the weather and the elements. He kept to the forests or loitered around barns and outbuildings. Occasionally someone would report seeing him in one or the other of the church graveyards, peering intently at certain grave plots—pulled there, perhaps, by some remaining instinct surviving his derangement.

It seemed that Bertrand wasn't enough, for soon a second weight began to oppress the community's conscience—a literal weight this time.

Strange things began happening on the road between Rehobeth and New Salvation churches. As Silas Mooney was riding by the Rehobeth graveyard one spring night, his wagon suddenly lurched over to the right, as if a heavy weight were holding it down. Silas' horse stopped short. When Silas urged him on, the horse strained as if he were pulling an extra-heavy load. He pulled the wagon, still tilted to one side, but the going was mighty slow. When they reached the New Salvation graveyard, the wagon sprang back to normal.

Caleb Strong had the same thing happen to him the next night, only he was going in the opposite direction. As his wagon pulled in front of New Salvation Church, it suddenly sank to the left. When Caleb got out to see why the wagon had tilted that way, he could find no cause. His poor horse huffed and puffed from that point on until they came to the Rehobeth graveyard, when the wagon suddenly jolted back to its original position.

Other people had similar experiences. Some said it was as if an invisible but heavy ghost hopped aboard their wagons or buggies and rode along for a while. A few people flicked their whips or kicked through the space above the weighted point where a person logically would have been, but they felt nothing.

Never would the ghost ride further than the graveyards. Often, with the through travelers, the ghost would ride all the way from one graveyard to the other. Sometimes he would board at a point in between, indicating that a local traveler had turned off at that point, leaving the ghost stranded until the next vehicle came along. The heavy ghost never harmed anyone. All he wanted was a ride between the two graveyards.

No one doubted that it was the ghost of old Ephraim Tucker. Why not, they asked. Since Ephraim's bones had been jostled and toted about so much, how could his ghost help being confused as to his final resting place? Especially when his name and the names of his wife and son were clearly marked on stones in both graveyards. It was confusing enough to the natives, let alone to strangers or ghosts.

Most people traveling these roads experienced the ghost at one time or another. They often talked about it, and some even recorded it in their diaries. It was not uncommon for someone to write, "The ghost rode part way home with us yesterday."

Uncle Jake Crowder, a patriarch of the Uwharries, experienced the ghost many times. Said he, "It got so my hoss, Rhodie, ever time he came nigh them graveyards, would sorta slow up and brace hisself and git his second wind, ready to dig harder when the ghost got on to ride with us."

It was Uncle Jake who reported a strange occurrence involving the ghost. One time, in the middle of the day, while the ghost was riding with him along a straight stretch of road without any turn-offs, they overtook Bertrand shambling along the road. The ghost hopped off abreast of him. Bertrand stopped walking, and his mouth broke into a broad grin and his arms reached out as if in greeting. Uncle Jake said it looked like a real joyful reunion.

One night Bertrand attracted the attention of a number of prominent families by rapping on their windows and doors and shaking his head woefully when they answered his knock.

They found him the next day about noon, lying dead on the

The Heavy Hitchhiker   127 ground exactly on the center of the grave he had picked out for himself, beside that of his father in the Rehobeth cemetery. He lay on his back, his hands folded neatly across his chest, his outstretched feet and legs close together. It appeared that he had lain down there, prepared himself the way he wanted, and expired naturally.

The members of Rehobeth Church buried him there beside his father in the spot he had selected.

Folks wondered if there would be two invisible hitchhiking ghosts now. But there were not. Old Ephraim's ghost kept on riding, out of habit for one thing, they guessed, and out of loyalty. He now had to visit a wife in one graveyard and a son in the other, eternally dividing his time between them.

The churches and the graveyards have faded now, and no one knows what happened to the money that was to have endowed one of them. The road between the two graveyards is submerged under the waters of Badin Lake, which flings many fingers into the loneliest parts of the Uwharries. There have been no reports of an invisible but heavy hitchhiker catching rides on the motorboats speeding across the cove. It may be that the ghost of old Ephraim Tucker is simply biding its time until liberated from the imprisoning waters.

BLACK MATHIE

THE RIDER WHO stopped at the Carolina plantation home at the edge of the Uwharrie Mountains looked as if he had ridden long and hurriedly, without sufficient food and rest. Though he was not an unusually large man, his roan mare sagged tiredly in the middle. The skin on the man's face had peeled in splotches from repeated exposure to the Southern sun. Dense whiskers failed to hide a lumpy scar on his cheek. One hand removed a dusty cap from his red hair, mottled now by streaks of gray. He dismounted stiffly, and his eyes squinted to appraise the farm. This looked like the place, but so had many others. An old Negro man watched from near the barn, and other Negroes worked in the fields nearby. When he saw two Negro women emerge at the rear of the big house, he led his horse forward.

"My name's Caroney," he said crisply. "Is your white mistress inside?" The women shook their heads. "How about your white master, is he here?" Again a negative answer.

Puzzled, Caroney continued. "I'm looking for a young white woman, the mistress of a plantation, who lived around here back during the war. She had long hair and pretty blue eyes and was a real elegant lady." He wiped his forehead with his dusty cap. "Do you know of this woman?"

The Negro women looked at each other, alarm flashing in their eyes. Before Caroney could stop them, they hurried into the house.

This must be the place, he thought. His eyes raked over the big house, the barn, the sheds, the shops, the granary, and the cluster of slave quarters off to one side. They looked vaguely familiar. His mind tried hard to remember. Then his eyes settled on a spot of dense woods across a field where a rutted road dipped into a rocky hollow. Those woods . . . was that where . . . ? There was one way to satisfy his curiosity and perhaps to ease his conscience. He mounted his horse and rode straight for the woods, heedless of the Negroes, who had stopped their field work to stare at him.

He had not gone far into the woods before he saw it and knew his search was ended. There stood the tiny, secluded log cabin, pine branches sweeping the roof, one corner green with moss. He approached it slowly, dazedly. The door yielded with a screech. His nervous breathing and his pounding heart echoed inside the four bare walls which mocked him. He leaned his head against the wall, and memories, elusive and long hidden, overwhelmed him.

The Union cavalry detachment, commanded by a young, dapper, redheaded lieutenant, had descended upon the plantation late one summer afternoon, just in time to glimpse a young white woman clinging to the back of a huge Negro man as a horse carried them into the woods near where a wagon road led down a slope into a rocky hollow. The lieutenant called to four of his men, and they gave pursuit. The chase ended at this secluded cabin.

A fierce old Negro man with a leveled shotgun met them at the door. "Don't come no closer, soldiers," he boomed, "or one of you is gonna die right dere."

The horsemen stopped. "Look, Negro," the lieutenant said, "you haven't a chance. You're outnumbered. You know that. Put down that gun and step aside. It will go easier with you."

But the Negro held his gun in firing position. "De first one of you dat moves forrard is a daid man," he warned. "Now all of you turn around and go back and leave us alone."

The lieutenant gripped his reins tighter. He glanced at his men, Hank and Luther on the left, Clyde and James on the right. They were good soldiers, personal friends, all from the same home town back North, where they had played together as boys, gone to school together, and worked together. All had joined the Union Army at the same time and had been allowed to serve in the same unit. Already they had weathered some of the hottest battles of the Civil War. Singly and collectively, they had saved the lieutenant's life more than once during the bedlam of battle. He hated to sacrifice a life, any life, especially that of one of his trusted buddies. Yet he couldn't let this lone Negro thwart them.

"Rush him!" he barked. All the horses and men lunged forward simultaneously.

At the crack of the black man's gun, Hank clutched his arm and toppled off his horse. Then the soldiers were upon the Negro before he had time to dart back inside. Within seconds they had knocked him senseless to the ground.

Ignoring the bleeding Negro and the wounded soldier, the lieutenant drew his sidearm and cautiously entered the cabin. A sharp lick on his cheek knocked him off balance, and he wheeled to see a pretty young white woman, her face contorted in rage, coming at him with an upraised fire poker. Easily he dodged her rush and kicked at her ankles with his heavy boot. She tripped and fell on the floor and lay there sobbing.

He walked back outside the door, his face bleeding. "You men go on back to the house, and I'll be along later. Take that black man with you and execute him. And I don't care if you play with him awhile first."

"No!" screamed a voice from the doorway. The woman attempted to rise. Tears streaked her cheeks. "No, please, don't you harm Black Mathie!"

By this time Black Mathie had regained consciousness and risen shakily to his feet. When his eyes focused on the woman, he cried out and lunged forward. The soldiers had to struggle to restrain him.

"What has you done to my missus?" he cried. His old eyes blazed as he wrenched mightily to free himself. "If you has hurt her, Lawd hep me, I'll git you. I'll make you pay for it. You lay a hand on her and you'll rue de day you was boan. De massah, he tole me to guard her wid my life, and dat's what I aims to do."

"Take this black devil out of my sight before I blow out his foolish brains," the lieutenant said, turning back to the woman.

The intenseness of Black Mathie's plea stopped him.

"Please, dear Cap'n," begged the black man, sinking to his knees and clasping his hands before him. "Please don't harm dat po' woman. Have your pleasure by torturin' me. But let dat po' little woman go. She ain't evah done nothin' to desarve no punishment. Take me and let her go, won't you, Suh?"

The sneer on the officer's mouth and the steel in his eyes gave the answer. Then the tone of Black Mathie's voice changed to an ominous threat.

"If you harms dat po' woman, I'll git even with you, Cap'n. I'll git you. No matter what you does to me or what happens to me, I'll git you for it. I'll git you. Some time, some how, some place, I'll git you. All of you. You'll all pay. I swears befo' de Lawd, I'll git you."

A gunstock slamming into his head from behind ended the black man's fervent shouting. They slung his inert form over a horse's rump, and the group headed out of the woods.

The woman tried to slip aside and dash away, but the officer caught her to him and pulled her into the cabin. When he left a short time later, he could hear her sobbing within. He made sure to lock the cabin door before joining his buddies at the big house.

For the next few weeks the lieutenant kept the woman captive in the hidden cabin on her own plantation. On his frequent visits there, he loved to torment her with detailed descriptions of how his soldiers had tortured Black Mathie and subjected him to indignities before ending his life with a fusillade of bullets. It had happened after supper one night in the presence of some of the other Negroes. Until his last breath, Black Mathie had kept threatening to get even with the lieutenant and his men.

Because of a change in Union plans, the lieutenant was ordered to move out abruptly and alone to a new assignment. He hastily bade goodby to his four special friends and left the captive woman for their enjoyment. The lieutenant never saw or heard from his friends again—neither during the remainder of the war nor afterward.

Now, Caroney rode slowly out of the woods and back to the plantation home. He told the old Negro at the barn—Old Pete he said his name was—that he would sleep in the barn. The next morning he asked Old Pete about his former master and mistress.

"De Massah, he dropped on de battlefield under Yankee fire," Old Pete said. "De Missus, Miz Matilda, she was killed by de Yankee cavalry soldiers dat found her in de cabin. Dey tormented her and mistreated her and ravaged her shamefully. She lingered sick for weeks, and den she died. She lies buried out yonder. Ol' Black Mathie —one of us—he tried to protect Miz Matilda lak de massah told him, but de soldiers killed him, too."

Caroney found the grave, and as he examined the marker he could sense the Negroes watching him from afar with growing interest. Then he went back to Old Pete with another question.

"I was through here during the war. I had four soldier buddies with me. Good friends. I had to leave suddenly and was separated from them. I never saw them again. They didn't return home after the war. There is no record of their having been killed or captured, and they weren't the type of men to desert. Their families are very concerned and want me to find out what happened to them. Can you, or anyone here, tell me anything?"

Old Pete shook his head slowly. But his eyes were suddenly much brighter.

Before the day ended, Caroney made up his mind to stay on the plantation, to rest up awhile, and to look around for some clues to the disappearance of his buddies. He learned from Old Pete that there were no descendants and apparently no heirs to the plantation and that the Negroes were former slaves who had remained because they had no other place to go. Caroney decided that he would stay on and operate the farm, buying it if necessary. Without giving the Negroes much chance to object, Caroney assumed some of the chores and began issuing mild instructions. Within a few days he was sleeping in the big house, and the Negro women were cooking for him.

For the next year or so, the farm, once a model of Southern agricultural enterprise, regained some of its former dignity under this arrangement. But then, another type of decline set in.

Lacking companionship, Caroney attempted to smother his growing discontent in drink, then in carousing, then in backbreaking labor. But he found that none of these antidotes afforded appeasement for the uneasy restlessness burning ever hotter inside him.

Almost every evening, after a lonely supper in the big house, Caroney would tell Old Pete to hitch up his roan to the buggy. Then, beginning in the cool dusk of evening, he would ride for hours along the wagon roads in the valley, stopping at each household to ask the people if they knew anything about his missing friends. On each nocturnal buggy drive, Caroney traveled a road which led him through a narrow trough between two hills known as "Rocky Hollow." The hillsides sloped steeply there, and the presence of rock strata prevented all but the sturdiest of shrubs and vines from gaining foothold. When a traveler dipped into the depression of Rocky Hollow, especially at night, he entered a world seemingly isolated from reality. It was into this strangeness that Caroney was drawn irresistibly every night, even though he might start out in a different direction to avoid the place.

Old Pete and the other stoic-faced Negroes began to notice gradual changes in Caroney. Worry put deeper lines in his face. He began mumbling to himself. His shoulders failed to square up to their former dignity. Ofttimes his hands trembled violently as Old Pete handed him the reins.

As the summer wore on and the buggy rides continued, the Negroes had good reason to believe that Caroney was slowly being driven insane by something he experienced on his rides.

One moonless July night when he returned from his ride, Caroney cracked up. Old Pete practically had to drag the panicky man to the side of the barn, where he sobbed, screamed, cursed, and babbled a frenzy of disconnected words about a ghost he had seen in Rocky Hollow.

Unknown to Caroney, other Negroes listened in the shadows.

"I s-saw the head of a man grinning at me down there in the rocks," he gasped, shaking. "Just a man's head without a body. A Negro's head—bright, glistening, and glowing. It's always there beside the road in front of me. It sneers at me with contempt. Sometimes it opens its mouth and spits at me. I've seen it for days. And every time it's a little bigger."

Despite his fear, Caroney was unable to stop his nightly buggy rides. Each time at dusk when he accepted the reins of the waiting horse and buggy, Caroney looked like a man walking to face a firing squad. And each night when he returned to the barn to turn over the buggy to Old Pete, he looked as if he had been shattered by a confrontation with a ghost.

Unknown to Caroney, several of the Negro men began slipping down to the hillsides above Rocky Hollow to watch in the moonlight as the tormented white man drove through the place in his buggy. Invariably, he would lash his horse and attempt to hurry through. But each time, the horse would slow to a crawl, despite his urging. Every night, when the Negroes watched the fascinating spectacle, they could hear Caroney yelling for the ghost to get out of his way and leave him alone—a ghost unseen by them but apparently quite real to Caroney.

"Get outta my way and leave me alone, you black devil," he would screech. "What do you want with me? Why do you keep pulling me down here every night to look at your stinking, grinning face? Why can't you stop hounding me and let me live in peace?"

Each night, upon returning to the barn, Caroney jerkily reported to Old Pete and the unseen audience of other Negroes. The grinning, glowing head of the black devil had become four times larger than a normal man's head. Soon it was as large as a rain barrel.

"It's always there, on the road, right in front of my horse," he babbled. "The face is getting bigger and meaner looking. It's full of sarcasm and hate. It snarls at me. I even see it in my sleep. It's driving me crazy."

Caroney claimed that the grinning ghost of Rocky Hollow got so big that it tried to open its mouth and bite him as he passed in his horse and buggy.

Finally one night Caroney returned hysterical. He demanded that Old Pete drive the buggy through Rocky Hollow and report what he saw. Old Pete did so and, of course, saw nothing unusual. This angered Caroney, and he accused the old man of lying. He called for another Negro to make the trip. The second man reported the same thing. Caroney went staggering to the big house, mumbling incoherently.

The next time he came to take his buggy ride, Caroney demanded that Old Pete ride with him in the buggy. Reluctantly and only to humor the deranged white man, Old Pete sat down in the buggy, and they wheeled away just as the moon rose over the trees. The closer they came to the hollow, the more tense and nervous Caroney became. As they entered the hollow, Caroney stood up in the open buggy and lashed the horse.

"There it is!" he cried, pointing. "There it is! You see it? Right there in front of the horse! Don't you see the big glowing head of that black nigger grinning at me? It's shining bright as the moon!"

Old Pete shook his head. "Dey ain't nothin' dere. I don't see nothin' lak you talk about."

Caroney collapsed after that and apparently resigned himself to the spell the ghost had on him. He began to mumble to Old Pete how the ghost was getting so huge it filled the roadway.

"It's trying to eat me," he whispered to the old man one night after

he returned weak and shaky from the hollow. "It's trying to open up its mouth and swallow me and the buggy."

A few nights later Caroney babbled out words which satisfied the Negroes that he at last realized the identity of the ghost haunting him. "It's that black devil I had killed around here during the war. He swore he'd get me. But I never dreamed he'd do it this way."

On the night of Caroney's demise, the Negroes were again on the hillside above Rocky Hollow, waiting to hear the agonized cries of the white man as he faced his nightly battle with his ghostly nemesis. From their vantage point the Negroes could see each end of the hollow, but not the middle portion. They watched Caroney's shadowy form in the moonlight now as he stood up tall in the buggy to lash his horse as he entered the hollow. They heard his screeching cries for the black devil to go away and leave him.

Then abrupt silence broke Caroney's shouting, not only in mid-sentence, but in mid-word. The Negroes looked at each other and nodded.

In a few minutes, the horse and buggy emerged at the far end of the hollow, and the horse stopped to nibble at bushes. There was no sign of Caroney.

One of the Negroes lit a long-handled pine torch, and the group slowly descended the hill and walked the length of Rocky Hollow, looking carefully for the white man. They found nothing. There was no hole or crevice large enough for him to have fallen into, no rock or bush or log big enough to hide him. He had simply vanished there in the hollow. The Negroes led the horse and buggy back up the road to the barn. That night they all slept with a vast relief.

At daybreak, the Negroes went back to Rocky Hollow and searched it and the surrounding territory thoroughly. No sign of Caroney was ever found. It appeared that the ground had just opened up and swallowed him.

When they returned to the barn, Old Pete chuckled.

"Well, I reckon dat's de last Yankee. Black Mathie is even, now, and can rest in peace."

His big knife whacked a fresh notch beside four older ones in the log over the stable door.

Caroney disappeared almost a century ago. But Rocky Hollow still exists.

If you are a Yankee of recent extraction, and particularly one with a guilty conscience, the natives advise against prowling around the lonely laurel-choked ravine, especially after sunset. You never can tell when the desire for further vengeance may reactivate the ghost of Black Mathie.

THE GHOST OF FOUNDERS' COLLEGE

THE FIRST TIME Harpy Lowrance glimpsed the girl in front of Chambers Hall at Founders' College, she captivated his interest and a large part of his heart. For one thing, she was breathtaking, with long black hair hourglassed at the back of her neck, teasing green eyes, a laughing face all sunny and smiling, a tight-waisted dress, and the stamp of Southern aristocracy plainly upon her. For another thing, Founders' was strictly an all-boys' school, and there had probably never been a girl there before.

As he drew near, she glided behind one of the tall round columns. He followed, but she was gone. He walked around the columns again, then out to the shrub-shouldered corner of the building. There was no girl in sight. It wasn't likely that she had gone inside, but he searched through the front part of the big building anyway, without success. It troubled him. He had seen her so plainly. And, of course, he wanted to see again a girl of such classic beauty.

That night in his upstairs room in Chambers Hall, Harpy mentioned the incident to his roommates, Louie and Younts, and asked if they had seen such a girl. They had not, and both were skeptical.

"We've only been here two weeks, and you're already having hallucinations," Louie said. "Don't let the professors know you've seen a beautiful girl here, or they'll hold a witch hunt. Remember the lectures? 'You are here to study medicine,'" he mimicked, "'to become doctors, to alleviate human misery and ailments, and to serve your fellowman. . . . You are not here to study women. Women are a distraction. That's why there are none here. So be prepared to get women off your mind for the next four years.' Why I'll bet there's never been a girl inside this monkish building. Except maybe the female cadavers. Hey!" His voice grew excited and fiendish. "Maybe what you saw was the ghost of a female cadav!"

But Harpy kept on seeing the girl around Chambers in succeeding weeks and months. Occasionally some of the other boys glimpsed her, too. She was usually in front of the building around the tall columns, sometimes on the stairway inside, and now and then at the front window. But always, when they rushed in for a closer look, she was gone.

The ghost of a female cadaver? Harpy shrugged his shoulders. Whoever she was, he would like to get to know her better.

Harpy knew that he could see the girl better and more often than the other boys. At each encounter, the attraction between them grew stronger. Often in the evenings he lingered around the front of the colonnaded building, hoping she would appear. Sometimes she did. Always he spoke to her, but she never answered, acknowledging him only with a lovely smile into which he read much tender meaning.

Once he was only a step or two away. She was so very desirable. Impulsively he stepped closer, his arms outstretched to enfold her in a tender embrace. But his eager arms closed onto nothingness, and she was gone. And then he knew what she was. It caused him much unrest.

Harpy talked with Professor Rudkin, who had been at Founders' as long as anyone.

"Yes, we've had a number of reports of the girl being seen here in past years," Rudkin said, letting Harpy hold his papers while he huffed on his eyeglasses and cleaned them. "We call her Louise. Some people can see her, and some can't. But it usually takes a boy with a special knack—clairvoyance, perhaps—to see her repeatedly, as you claim to have done. Stick with it, son, and maybe you can figure her out.

"Is she a ghost? Probably. But who knows? What is she doing

here? We've wondered for decades. Most of us on the staff know the girl is seen here. But, officially, the college doesn't recognize it. Wouldn't be very dignified or scholarly or favorable, would it—sanctioning a female ghost at a men's college? So whatever new knowledge you glean about her during your stay here, handle it with the first and most basic lesson you should learn—discreetness."

But Louise didn't go much for discreetness. She must have missed Harpy terribly during summer vacation because, beginning in the fall of his second year at Founders', she went practically everywhere he did on the campus. She'd sit in a vacant chair in the dining room and watch Harpy eat. Occasionally she'd go with him to the classroom. Almost always when he stood to recite, she'd be sitting unobtrusively at the back of the room, silently beaming at him and boosting him. Under her stimulation, his classroom performances amazed his instructors.

But there were inopportune times, too.

Louie and Younts grumbled about her appearing in the room when they were in various stages of undress. Sometimes, upon awakening in the morning, they would see her, apparently asleep, crumpled on the floor against one wall. Harpy began to wonder if that spot held some significance.

At least once a month, some uninformed, strait-laced professor would glimpse Louise around Chambers Hall, gasp in disbelief, and call for a quick shakedown of the building. Of course, they could never find the girl. But sometimes they would put the hall on probation and restrict the boys to the building, despite their pleas and protests.

Once Louise appeared briefly on the edge of the stage during an assembly program in which Harpy participated. The boys immediately burst into applause. At another assembly, when a freshman was trying to read an assigned paper on the advantages of an all-male college for studying and concentrating on serious subject matter, Louise impishly materialized behind him and peered over his shoulder for a moment. The boys couldn't resist. They let out whistles and catcalls, throwing the professors into a state of alarm.

One of the worst peccadillos involved old Mrs. Symington, a fiery dowager whose late industrialist husband had left her millions, much of which she had earmarked for generous endowments to Founders', which her husband had helped establish and her son had attended. On her annual inspection tour of the college, she and President McGrath stopped late one afternoon to admire the stateliness and tranquillity of old Chambers Hall.

Abruptly, a pretty young woman flitted across in front of the structure and vanished behind the big columns.

Mrs. Symington gasped and pointed. "That young woman! What . . . ?"

At that precise instant, a young man dashed into view, following the same course the girl had taken.

Mrs. Symington recoiled. When she recovered, she lashed into a tirade. "A student chasing a girl into his dormitory! McGrath! How can you condone such behavior? It's scandalous, positively scandalous! I demand that you find both of them immediately and punish them. Right now!"

They found the student with no trouble. It was Harpy. He had simply been trying to stop Louise before she got back to her favorite haunt to disappear. Spurred by Mrs. Symington's indignant demands, they searched the big building methodically and thoroughly. But they found no girl. Mrs. Symington went away muttering darkly and accusing McGrath of underhandedness, hanky-panky, and tainted moral leadership. The president developed ulcers and alienated most of his associates by his irritability while he waited to see if the incident had jeopardized the Symington endowment.

They called Harpy on the carpet and threatened immediate suspension or expulsion if he did not hastily disassociate himself from the ghost or at least get her to tone down her wild capers.

Everyone knew that Harpy was the key to Louise. He had the

proper psychic turn of mind to attract her. But influencing or controlling her was quite another matter. Nevertheless, Harpy became the center of an abrasive tug of war between the students, wanting to see more of Louise, and the administration, wanting to see less.

On bended knee, Harpy pleaded with Louise to control herself and to stop her mischievous and embarrassing materializations. Despite the close affinity between them, he was never sure whether she understood his plea or would co-operate if she did, considering her seniority here and her being an independent and flighty female and all. Besides, she had an exceedingly devoted following among the student body, having become their unofficial mascot and girl friend. She might not want to let all this fade away.

No other major ghost-caused catastrophe occurred, however, to embarrass the college, though there were some narrow misses. Louise continued to have quite a gay time teasing the boys and flirting with them around the dorms, especially around Chambers Hall, often causing Harpy great despair at her apparent disloyalty to him.

It was an honored tradition at Founders' for the top students in the graduating class to arrange interviews with leading practitioners in their areas of specialization. For some reason, Dr. J. Demetri Parnell, an alumnus of Founders', drew Harpy's attention. Harpy knew better than to disregard his intuition. His letter to the famous doctor in Baltimore brought a quick reply. Dr. Parnell was catching a train down to Raleigh to speak at a medical convention on the thirtieth. Could Harpy see him late that afternoon after the meeting?

Harpy took a train from Salisbury to Raleigh on the thirtieth, and the doctor met him in the lobby of his hotel. He appraised Harpy with keenly probing blue eyes. His reassuring smile must have been used on thousands of patients, but Harpy sensed his sincerity, and it gave him confidence.

The old doctor nodded his shock of frosty hair toward the dining room. "Let's talk while we eat," he suggested in the doctor-to-patient manner with which one does not argue.

The professional talk ended with the meal. Harpy was amazed at the man's effortless answers and his concise exposition of everything he mentioned. Then they went up to the doctor's hotel room. The old man made himself comfortable. He took a snort of gin, stuffed and lit a big pipe, sank into an overstuffed chair, propped his slippered feet on the edge of the bed, and looked long at the ceiling.

Harpy decided to ask him about the ghost. He told the doctor about Louise, about the strange attraction that seemed to exist between them, and asked him if, in the light of his distinguished experience, he could offer any explanation for the phenomenon.

Dr. Parnell smiled softly, nostalgically. You could almost see his thoughts spinning back through the years. "Louise is not her real name, but never you mind about that."

He fell silent again and swung around to stare hard at Harpy, thinking, weighing, evaluating something. The scales must have tipped in Harpy's favor, for he settled back again, satisfied, and his eyes locked on the ceiling.

"Old Founders' College. I was there about forty years ago. Took my medical there. Kinda rough on us back in those days. Each student—and there weren't so many of us in a class back then—had to get his own cadaver and his own human skeleton for laboratory and classroom study. That was in the days when grave-robbing flourished. All those little graveyards around the Uwharries were targets. Lots of people knew it. Many others suspected it. Most open-minded people accepted it as long as you were discreet, didn't offend anyone, and never let a bereaved family know that you had appropriated the body of a loved one. The college officials, department heads, and instructors knew it, too. While they stressed the discreet part, they never asked any questions when a fresh body appeared in the boiling vat and a new skeleton danced from its wire . . . unless there were repercussions.

"Three of us went by buggy to Salisbury one Saturday to see a minstrel show. There, we read in the paper and heard people talking about the death of a pretty young woman in her early twenties, the daughter of one of the most prominent families in the state. Her funeral that afternoon had been attended by VIP's from far and near.

"If we hadn't passed by that new grave in the big cemetery on our way out of town late that night, the idea probably would never have occurred to us. But we did. It was on toward midnight. All of us had had a few beers after the show and were feeling adventurous. The whole thing was Tip's idea. He was the only one without a cadaver. He had helped Theodore and me get ours earlier, so we felt obligated to lend assistance, though we should have known better than to tamper with the grave of such an important person.

"We found the cemetery toolshed and borrowed shovels and a pick. Then we set to work enlarging the new grave to expose one end of the casket. It was pretty hard work, but we finally made it. We broke open the end of the casket, reached in, and grabbed the corpse by the hair of her head. We pulled her out, wrapped her in a blanket, and put her on the floorboard of the buggy. Then we filled up the grave again, replaced the tools, and drove on back to school just ahead of a bad rainstorm, which covered our tracks. We got there about dawn, too tired even to light a fire and boil the flesh off the body. So we covered her up on the floor in our room and went to bed. We slept most of the day. When we finally got up, we were so blooming lazy that we decided the body would keep another night until we could get the handyman to do the boiling for us on Monday.

"But we didn't figure on the damage the rainstorm had caused in the cemetery. Jarvis Duncan, another classmate, had been in Salisbury that Sunday, and he got back to school about dark and told us about it. The whole town was buzzing mad and shocked with outrage. The family had gone back Sunday morning to look at the grave and the flowers. They saw what we had done, because the rain—a real trash-mover—had washed out all that loose soil and had exposed the busted end of the empty casket. Some of the womenfolk fainted dead away.

"They called the law, the High Sheriff, their lawyer, and the undertaker. The father of the missing dead girl tongue-lashed the officials into quick action to find the 'nefarious body-snatching scum' who would commit such an unspeakable act. He swore eternal vengeance upon the guilty parties.

"Right away they began to suspect that it had been some of the Founders' College medical students eager for a fresh corpse, especially one of such impressive background and prominence.

"Jarvis knew we three had been in town the night before, and, as he eyed the bulky pile of blankets on the floor, he said that he thought we might be interested to know that the father and all those officials were on their way with guns and search warrants to comb the college to a fare-thee-well. If they found that corpse, there'd be hell to pay. The father's anger and grief combined to make him maniacal, and he was likely to shoot anyone he thought might be responsible for his dead daughter's desecration. If the culprits weren't shot, they'd probably be summarily kicked out of school, prosecuted in court, and sentenced to hard labor in the pen. The image and prestige of the school would suffer woefully. No one wanted that to happen. Not after all those lectures on ethics and discreetness. Jarvis suggested some speedy and clever hiding of the body—assuming such was around—which nobody denied. Then he left, saying that he didn't know how much time we had, but that he'd try to keep on the lookout.

"We knew our only hope lay in hiding the corpse where it would never be found. And we had to do it right there in Chambers Hall, for we couldn't risk taking the body out again. The attic seemed the logical place. We lived in a room on the second floor at the front. Attached to the wall right outside our door was an old iron ladder, which led to a scuttle hole in the ceiling. We had a coil of rope, so we tied it securely to the body, got ourselves a lantern and a hammer, and climbed the ladder into the attic, pulling the body up before replacing the trap door. It was dark as pitch, but we had work to do nonetheless. We dragged the body out on the low ledge over those tall columns in front of the building. The two columns in the center were mostly fake ones for looks. They extended up into the attic, and the tops were boarded over. We pried off some of the boards, and, since the body was already fastened to the rope, we lowered it down inside one of the hollow columns, the second one from the left, which must've been three feet in diameter. We let the body go all the way to the bottom. Then we replaced the boards as quietly as possible, took time to stick a few cobwebs back in place, and went back down to the room.

"We hadn't been back more'n a few minutes when we heard sharp voices and Jarvis yelling out greetings. Tip and I moseyed downstairs, leaving Theodore in the room pretending to study. The irate father was a big, impressive man with graying hair and a mustache. He carried a long-barreled gun cradled in his arm. With him were a silver-starred lawman, an unctuous undertaker, and a neatly-dressed man who looked like a lawyer. In tow, they had Founders' president, Dr. Cyrus Moffett, and the head of the Medical Department, old Dr. Sousa Prince. Both were scared. Muscles twitched on their faces and their voices quavered. Both kept insisting that the search was quite useless, that no student or representative of Founders' would stoop to such a dastardly deed as the visitors were insinuating.

"But search they did. From one end of the building to the other. They were thorough, too. They looked closely in every classroom and closet, in every laboratory cabinet and drawer, in all the dorm rooms, under the beds—in every place large enough to conceal a body. When they got to the hallway outside our room, the father looked up at the ladder leading to the scuttle hole. He told the sheriff to climb up and check. The officer climbed the ladder and stuck his head and shoulders through, holding his light high inside. He said there were too many thick cobwebs for anything to have passed through there recently.

"Well, they didn't find the body, and the searchers gruffly apologized for the trouble they had caused and then left. You know, we were so scared by that close shave that we never attempted to recover the body but left it right there where it was, at the bottom of the hollow shaft.

"And we never did tell anyone. The president and the faculty never found out about it, though they might have suspected that something was afoot. Now Tip and Theodore are both dead. Jarvis, too, in all likelihood, since he went to Africa twenty years ago and hasn't been heard from since. I'm the last one who knows the story, and I'll be fading away one of these days right soon. I'm glad our paths crossed, young fellow, because such a heritage as this at Founders' needs to be revived and perpetuated—if only among a select few. But keep ethics in mind. Even at this late date, I wouldn't want any scandal or anything unsavory to blot the reputation of our alma mater. So remember how to be discreet."

Though he didn't let the old man know it as he thanked him and left, Harpy's initial reaction was one of amazement and incredulity. Louise? Of course! This explained Louise. An attractive young woman in her twenties? That was Louise.

Back at Founders', Harpy approached old Chambers Hall in the afternoon sun and scrutinized anew the tall ivied columns. He concentrated on the one Dr. Parnell had specified, the second one from the left, noting how the top vanished into the woodwork overhead and the base snugged into a solid granite block. He felt the rough surface of the massive pillar and rapped it with his knuckles. The only way to get inside would be to go down through the top.

"I know who you are now, honey, and I know how to liberate you," he whispered into the ivy leaves.

But should he? Should he remove those bones and deprive the college of its ghost? A college needed a romantic legend to give it individuality and distinction. This was his last semester at Founders', and soon he'd be leaving Louise anyway. Old Chambers Hall would probably be slated for demolition in a modernization program one of these years, too.

That night he told Louie and Younts the old man's story, part of which had occurred in the very room they occupied. Both were skeptical.

"Too fantastic," Louie scoffed. "The old man's mind is off; his imagination is running haywire."

"Weird," Younts agreed. "But I can see you're gonna have to find out for yourself, so we'll help you."

They assembled some rope, a rope ladder, a gunny sack, a wrecking bar, flashlights, and a kerosene lantern. Late one night they used a stepladder borrowed from the maintenance shop to reach the old iron wall ladder, the bottom part of which had been cut off nine feet from the floor to reduce its invitation to adventurers. With their gear in hand, they clambered up, shoved aside the protesting cover over the entrance hole, and fanned a path through decades of spider webs. They paused at the top of a huge column covered solidly with wooden timbers.

Their light showed several boards that might have been removed once in the long ago. The wrecking bar pried them up squawkingly. Harpy leaned over the void and played the beam of his powerful flashlight below.

"Something down there, all right," he said, "but I can't see well enough to tell what it is. I'll have to go down there."

As a precaution against encountering foul air at the bottom of the deep shaft, they tested it by lowering a lighted lantern to the bottom. It burned steadily and normally.

Then Harpy tied the end of the rope ladder to a beam, lowered it into the column, and started down, the flashlight in his hand, the sack tucked in his belt. With a rope tied tightly around his middle, he descended deeper as Louie paid out the slack.

Soon he announced that he had reached the bottom. "She's down here, too," came his excited voice. "The bones seem to be in good shape. I'll put them in the sack."

In a few minutes more, Harpy emerged at the top, carefully holding a sackful of bones. He removed a grinning skull to show his pals.

They replaced the timbers over the top of the shaft, left the attic, and went back to their room. For the next few weeks prior to his graduation, Harpy spent all his spare time with bone preservatives, wire, and pliers. Louie and Younts, who were also graduating, assisted him.

Several times that spring, before he left, Harpy lingered in the evenings around the front of Chambers Hall to find out if he could see or make contact with Louise again. With him he took two of her personal possessions that he had found with the bones—a signet ring with her initials carved plainly on the inner band and a gold cameo locket with her picture inside. But she never appeared. There was no response to the urgent messages his mind and heart were sending out to the domain of the spirits.

Though the instructors and the hierarchy at Founders' wouldn't admit it then or now, one day an extra skeleton appeared in a classroom. The assembly and wiring had been expertly done. The bones glistened and gleamed. No one ever found out its origin, but then, not many questions are asked about such things.

After he left Founders', Harpy became a famous surgeon, pioneering several major breakthroughs in his field. Though he's pushing retirement age now, Harpy hasn't slowed much, but he is redirecting some of his energies. Most of his private practice has been shifted to younger men. He has assumed various consultant positions and is about ready to hit the lecture circuit. Eager young med students like to quiz him about his stellar accomplishments and get him to talk about the good old days in medicine.

Harpy has been saving one story for the brilliant young undergraduate from Founders' College who will show up for an interview one day. The interview will conclude with an awkward personal question about a skeleton in one of the classrooms of the new Science Building. The student will almost swear that occasionally, when the lecture grows dull and the light dim, the skeleton transforms itself for a few seconds into an attractive young woman with a laughing face. Then Harpy will tell him about Louise.

Yes, and maybe he'll show the boy something, too.

With delicate blue-veined hands, Harpy unlocks a drawer in his private desk, unfolds a yellowed envelope, and extracts a velvet pouch that reveals a handsome cameo locket with a fine golden chain. He opens it. Inside is a picture of a Southern belle with aristocratic features and long black hair, hourglassed at the back.

Sometimes she smiles at him.